# Intimat...

TALKS WITH J. G. ...
AT BESHARA...

# Intimations

TALKS WITH J. G. BENNETT
AT BESHARA

With Introduction by
RASHID HORNSBY

BESHARA PUBLICATIONS

© 1975 The Estate of J. G. Bennett

Published by Beshara Publications
Swyre Farm, Aldsworth,
Gloucestershire

ISBN (H/C) 0 904975 03 7
(P/B) 0 904975 02 9

Designed and printed at
The Compton Press Ltd,
Compton Chamberlayne, Salisbury
Wiltshire

# Contents

*These chapters have been collected from transcriptions of tapes made from the talks with J. G. Bennett at Beshara, Swyre Farm, between 1972 and 1974. Beshara Publications is grateful for the help given by Elizabeth Bennett, Tony Blake and Penny Gibson in assembling these talks in a literal form.*

# Introduction

BY RASHID HORNSBY

J. G. Bennett was without doubt one of the truly outstanding men of
our time. There are and have been very few people who have totally
immersed themselves in the struggle for self-perfection, and who
have had the determination to reach the goal they have set themselves. It was to this struggle for self-perfection that J. G. Bennett
dedicated his life, and became an example to all around him. I am
sure that there could not be a perceptive seeker on this path who in
meeting him did not recognise his extraordinary qualities, which
were the signs of his own inner achievement. Unlike many, he found
and was in contact with the actual 'living' source from which the
teachings he had followed were able to be adapted and re-formulated
to the needs of the changing state of the world. He found and understood not only the key to the general condition of mankind, but was
also able to relate this knowledge specifically to the present world
situation. Convinced of the urgency of the need for real change at
this time, he taught that only a fundamentally different set of values
and a different motivation could save man from his present plight.
His whole life was directed to this end, of being able to show that
there is a different standpoint to life from the one we usually accept,
and that this other standpoint is the hope for the future. His last
years spent as Principal of the International Academy for Continuous
Education at Sherborne House were the culmination of this work.

There is a great difference between a man who takes on himself
the duty of changing the attitudes of people, who acts out his own
personal concern with the state of the world, and the man who has
and acts only according to an objective mission. I think it was evident
to all who really knew J. G. Bennett that he had an important mission in this world. He never thought of himself as something special,
but rather that he could only act and work in complete dependence
upon a higher power, and it is precisely this ability to act in depen-

dence upon a higher power that made him different from most men. In his late years he would often speak of the collaboration and help he had had in this work, and in particular his own strong connection with the Sufis of Central Asia, the 'Masters of Wisdom', the Haja Gân. This was not a reference to the Central Asia of Russia today, but to the spirit and the homeland of these 'Masters of Wisdom', who lived in that area from the ninth century on. And their world does not only include this material, physical world, but also the worlds of 'spiritual realities'. His comprehension of these other worlds, their realms and dimensions of thought, enabled him, while being completely involved with his work at Sherborne House, still to assert that he felt Beshara was complementary to his teaching at Sherborne.

Brought into contact at an early age with G. I. Gurdjieff, he became perhaps one of his closest and most highly regarded pupils, using what he had learnt from Gurdjieff as a basis for much of his later work. It seems that after the death of Gurdjieff, many of the former students and followers became convinced that they knew something special, or that they had some special position or responsibility to further Gurdjieff's work. Consequently many petty factions and arguments arose that almost destroyed the meaning and value of Gurdjieff's teaching. J. G. Bennett was aware how dangerous and misleading it is to create factions and to maintain that there are real differences between people, and thus kept himself as free as possible from any of these factions. It is perhaps this achievement that caused considerable animosity towards him, for he was the first to admit that he had more enemies than friends. Not being content to stop at what he had learnt from Gurdjieff, he used this knowledge as a tool to further his own evolution, and went on and on searching, meeting people and coming into contact with different ideas. It was only at the end of his life that he was given the greatest responsibility, which was to disseminate openly what he had learnt throughout his life to as many people as possible. He was adamant in his belief that the old system of teacher and pupil could not and should not continue in the form it had taken in the past. He saw that it was not possible or desirable in the present world situation, where the necessity for the dissemination of esoteric knowledge had obviously to take place on a global scale, if it is to prove affective. That is why he did not confine himself in the last years of his life to teaching only a small group of students, but concentrated on making the message of a proper spiritual attitude to life as widely available as he could. I know he became increasingly certain that the hope for the future lies with young people, and his understanding and concern with young people, particularly whilst he was at Sherborne was remarkable in itself. He was convinced that it was this generation that could bring a new vision to a world in grave danger of exterminating itself. Most people must realise that it is very easy to talk about 'man's condition', and how mankind should change consciously for the better, and that it is really quite another matter even to think in terms of bringing this about. It is precisely the process of 'becoming' what one should be that must concern us all, as is clearly shown from the discussions that form the content of this book.

J. G. Bennett was always duly cautious of talking about many things that he felt were too deep, too heavy and thus potentially dangerous for the average person. But I know that his experience at Sherborne convinced him that the post-war generations are by their nature capable of assimilating certain spiritual realities at a greatly accelerated rate. As he wrote in the Preface to 'Witness' — 'Our future depends upon those who see and can help others to see. The older generations, with few exceptions, are blind. Hope lies with the young; but they too must put short-term selfish aims aside and work for the future.' It is as if by necessity that the possibility of understanding what had previously been hidden and esoteric has been made easier for them. Convinced of the need to talk as freely and openly as possible on matters that would have perhaps remained more secret in the past, he sometimes shocked people used to thinking in more established ways. There are those who feel that greater restraint should be exercised in these matters, but this is because they have not yet understood the changes that must come about, and what we are in preparation for. If they understood what humanity is heading towards and the necessary steps that have to be taken these criticisms would appear very limited. There is a very urgent need for change, and it requires people who are prepared to sacrifice much to meet that end.

It was extraordinary how willing J. G. Bennett was to help in any way he could in the development of Beshara, despite the immense pressure of work at Sherborne House. He would always find time to come and talk, and I know that all who had the opportunity of hear-

ing and learning from him at Beshara are grateful and feel privi-
ledged. I also remember clearly his saying that it could not be an
accident that Sherborne House was only a few miles from Swyre
Farm, the first major Beshara Centre, and that he felt his mission was
in essence exactly the same as that of Beshara. We also coincided in
the opinion that it is imperative at this time that small self-sufficient
centres should be established around the world to which people can
come, not to join a sect or to listen to any particular guru or teacher,
but where the motivation should be for each person to pursue their
personal development and find what the responsibility of being
human entails. He was painfully aware that by and large those who
seek gurus and teachers seek only an identification of their own per-
sonality.

The talks which comprise this book exemplify the depth and
universality of this vision, and yet, they retain a clarity and sim-
plicity of expression that is hard to equal. The knowledge which we
are shown here relates in all cases to the primary and unique position
of man, with his capabilities of self-consciousness and self-perfection.
It also alludes to the even greater mystery expressed in the words
of *Giordano Bruno*, who was burnt along with all his works for saying, 'at the crossroads of the Horizon stands the Man'. Because of
this universal vision, J. G. Bennett was able to feel at home with all
people and never limited himself by belonging to, or orientating himself to any one particular expression. This is the standpoint of love
and compassion for all things, the standpoint of true knowledge, for
in this vision all existence and creation is contained within One
Unique Reality. And it is this vision, unrestricted by dogma and sec-
tarianism that is so important for anyone who wishes to see a world
united, conscious of its destiny, and founded on spiritual values
rather than personal greed. For as the Andalusian saint, Ibn al-'Arabi
so aptly put it . . . 'The Man of Wisdom, whatever may happen, will
never allow himself to be caught up with one definite form or belief,
because he is wise unto himself.'

In an age of difficulty and stress, with much at stake, it seems there
is no way that man can act and do anything to better this world if
he cannot reach what J. G. Bennett referred to as 'objective compassion'. In his own words, 'the real thing is to have this objective compassion, to say: "I must do something myself, and that, though small
in its material consequences, can be very, very large in its spiritual

consequences." These talks are examples of an attitude to existence, and indicate a way that is open to all who wish both to make something of themselves and provide a more optimistic outlook for generations to come. If man can learn to adopt an attitude to his existence which really incorporates the notion of a reciprocal responsibility to his Creator then such a change will come about, both individually and collectively, that life will become what J. G. Bennett tried throughout his life to show that it could be. But this is a very big step, although easy to talk about, and there are many other considerations that spring to mind. We are now only at the beginning and perhaps can only see a vague outline of what this different perspective might mean. And it is for this reason that the title given to this book is 'Intimations', for what words can express is very limited, but yet by them and our own correlation and understanding we may be shown the guidelines according to which we can base actions and lives.

Such knowledge should never be underestimated, neither should its power nor effect upon all that it touches, and any man who attains to this knowledge stands out against the horizon of this world long after he has gone. Such is the case with J. G. Bennett who has left us an imprint, an indication of Reality that all can profit by.

RASHID HORNSBY

*Bitez Yalisi,* 1975

# The World Situation

What I want to talk about with you is the state of this world in which we are and how we should look into the future. This is particularly relevant, in my opinion, to what you are doing here at Beshara and that's why I want to talk to you about it.

Everyone knows that we are in a state of transition, going from one kind of world to another. But is this all that we can know about it? It is usual now to speak of the New Age, or the Aquarian Age, which is simply an astrological interpretation of the cycles through which mankind passes. These, so far as I have been able to see from a lot of research into the changes that have come over the life of mankind in the past, do not accurately correspond to the astrological periods. Study of the Ice Ages shows evidence that the amount of sunlight reaching the earth on account of the general configuration of the solar system did not have as much influence on climate as one might expect. It had an influence, but not a primary influence. Similarly, if we look at these cycles of the Zodiac over the last ten or twelve thousand years, the timing does not exactly fit, and yet in some way they have a place. I have come to the conclusion that there is a certain reality in the influence of the general configuration of the solar system on the history of the earth, but there are also other factors to consider that are of a different order – possibly of a higher order, because, after all, the influences of the configuration of the planets are still within this existing world.

The way I look at it is that there has been a combination of influencing factors, part of which are predetermined by forces within the solar system, and part of which depend upon higher influences, influences from beyond the solar system. I am strengthened in this belief by what I know about man. We people also have two kinds of influences that determine the shape of our lives. One is connected with the influences under which we were conceived and born, our heredity, which determine the pattern of life that is open to us. We call it fate, and everyone knows how many things do come out in accordance with the pattern that is determined by competent astrologers. But there is also something else that is quite different in us, that is not determined in this way, that is outside the influences of the solar system – our destiny. Our destiny is what we are intended to find; if necessary, even to the extent of struggling against our own fate.

There are certain forces that will inevitably bring about changes in the conditions of life on this earth, but they're not wholly imposed on us, because there is also a higher destiny of mankind that depends upon whether or not we are able to respond to influences that are outside of the material world, outside of the solar system. Some such picture as this that I have formed in the course of many years of study of these things may seem to you to be saying very little, because some people venture to say very much more than this about the pattern of the world. I'm only saying what I have seen from my studies and from a lifetime of experience of these things, and from certain, perhaps intuitive, perceptions. But all of these together and every kind of interpretation points to the same conclusion, which is that we are now entering a new cycle in the life of mankind, and there is nothing really more important for any of us, than to try to understand what this means.

People feel very optimistic when they think that we're passing into the Aquarian Age because of the various kinds of favourable influences they associate with it. But they overlook that there are also influences which are quite threatening connected with the very same configuration, and it is not at all certain that the Aquarian pattern of itself will assure a favourable future to mankind. No, one must look more deeply behind this. The greater influences connected with the *destiny* of man on this earth – these work in very great cycles. After all, man has lived on this earth a very long time, compared with which the astrological cycles of two or three thousand years are hardly anything at all, and there have been very great changes in human life, not only changes in the environment and in the races of men, but even in the very species.

It is, for example, quite improbable that Neanderthal man could have a fertile crossing with the new man that has arisen on the earth. This idea you have probably all of you read about in various kinds of speculations. But let us suppose that we have to look at this seriously, as I believe we should; that we have really to look at this world, not in terms of just the visible forces and trends, but in terms of the factors much more difficult to discern and to recognise, because they represent influences that we are not at present conscious of. We are not even able to be conscious of them because we do not have the kinds of perceptions or the organs of perception that are needed. Perhaps it is better to say that very very few people on the earth at the present have these kind of perceptions; but perhaps a new kind of man is going to enter the earth in the course of not very great time, when there will be people with perceptions that are very different from those of almost all people of the present time.

This does raise the question – How will these people live? Will they be satisfied with the kind of institutions we have? Will they be able to live in a quite different way with one another than we're able to live? We live so very much on the outside, so very much dependent upon our senses, upon what we can see and hear and touch.

I speak with you and you depend upon sound, and perhaps even depend to some extent upon looking at me and seeing what I am saying. If I had not spoken at all, if I had said 'I'm sorry, tonight I'm not going to speak. You will have to read my thoughts;' you would probably have said 'Well, this is a bit hard. We're not quite up to that yet'. But, it still would have been true, that if I had sat in silence with you for half an hour, a great deal would have happened. We should have been aware of something happening between us that one is not aware of through words. These other forms of perception are not really so remote that they can't be awakened if one knows something about it. When you meditate together, when you meditate in silence, there is a communication. When you decide that you will spend a day, or two days, or more in complete silence with one another, you become aware that there is a closeness between people that comes in silence, that cannot be arrived at through words. So, it is not as if the possibility of a different kind of society, based not so much upon external communication as upon some kind of inner perception, is such a remote and fantastical idea. But, can we say anything more?

If we look back over the history of the world – and strangely enough we can now reconstruct the history of the world for the past thirty, forty or even fifty thousand years, with decreasing precision, of course, as we go back, but still with clearly defined landmarks, owing to new methods of dating and to the discovery of more and more of the traces left of earlier cultures – and we can see that there has been, not just a steady change running through the life of mankind, but two very different things, two very different trends, and these are both very instructive for us. One of these trends is that of accelerated change. This accelerated change, or accelerated evolution, has been a law ever since life has been on this earth. In the great changes – from the non-living to the primitive living states, from the living states to the cellular states, from those to the primitive plants, and animals, and so all the way through, until the mammals were reached, and then man and so on – every stage has taken far shorter time than the preceding stage. So things are going faster and faster, until now the movement is very rapid indeed, so rapid that profound changes take place in the life of man, and the life of this planet itself – not only of the human race but of the whole planet – within a single lifetime. Whereas the planet a hundred years ago was comfortably able to absorb all human activity without any observable trace of damage to it, now human activity is visibly damaging. This is a very enormous change. What we were doing on this earth as recently as a hundred years ago, was quite tolerable for this planet. That is the extraordinary thing, that in such a short space of time, there should have been such a very great change. This has to be taken into account: that we are living at the moment in a situation when the changes in the life of this planet are so rapid that it cannot continue as it is without there being a complete breakdown.

It is generally accepted and recognised that, in some way or other, this acceleration of change will have to stop. Until quite recently this question didn't even arise, but now it has got to be taken into account. Any thoughts we have about the future must take into account that we are in a period of not merely rapid, but accelerated change. We can only predict one of two things – either total disaster, or a change in the law under which the development of this planet is going. In other words, this acceleration must stop. It is like a plane in a nose dive. Only two things can happen to a plane in a nose dive – either it has to be pulled out of it, or it will be smashed to pieces. This is the first thing that history teaches us.

The other is the certainty that there are also cycles, that things have not gone uniformly, that there have been periods of very rapid change, followed by periods of stagnation, followed by periods of renewal. These cycles have been superimposed upon the general accelerating process, just as the waves of the sea are superimposed upon the movement of the tide. We see the rise and fall of the waves and we see the rising of the tide, and we know that at some moment the tide must cease to rise, because its momentum will have been exhausted. In the same way in the life of man, we see this rising of the tide of activity on the surface of this planet and something has got to change. But, all the same, one has to take account – because we are so small and our lives are so short – of the cycles. In other words, we are like children playing by the shore for whom the waves are very important – it is very frightening when a wave sweeps over you! These waves are like the short cycles of life. They last perhaps two thousand years. But there are greater waves.

I expect we have all sat by the shore and watched to see if it's true that every seventh wave is a specially large one. When I was told this as a child, it so fascinated me that I was determined to know whether it was true or not. And there is something like that, that from time to time the waves are greater, that is, the cycles are not the ordinary cycles of rise and fall of civilizations and cultures, but something greater in the life of man. The last very great change in the life of man occurred at the end of the Ice Ages, about ten thousand years ago, when the whole condition of life on this earth was profoundly changed. A very great part of the traces of earlier culture was wiped out. Some kinds of catastrophies, which we have no means yet of reconstructing, must have occurred – because earlier cultures left much greater traces. So we have many more traces of what happened eighteen to twenty, thirty thousand years ago, than we have of the period just preceding the end of the Ice Ages when many, many animals disappeared and a great part of the human race. According to traditions such major changes occur in long periods of time. There must be some very ancient memories that made people leave behind them this tradition or legend. Today, with our much more precise knowledge – with dating and with the examination of vast quantities of recorded material – we can see that ten to twelve thousand year cycles really do hold good on this earth. At least we can trace that twelve thousand, perhaps twenty-five and certainly thirty-seven thousand years ago the very great changes came. The greatest of all was thirty-seven thousand years ago, when our modern race of men appeared, and the Neanderthal man disappeared. Another

great thing happened twenty-five thousand years ago at the very
height of what is sometimes called the reindeer culture, when man's
civilisation reached an unprecedentedly high level, and art and in-
dustry and discovery must have been very advanced. In spite of the
very few traces that are left behind, there are enough to show that
there was knowledge then that was not attained again by mankind
until really quite recently. If the last great change happened ten
thousand years before Christ – that is, twelve thousand years ago,
the time of the ending of the Ice Ages and the beginning of the great
movements towards our modern languages, cultures and religions –
then maybe we are due for another change equally as great in the
way in which man lives on this earth. Or, possibly we may be due
for something that is even greater : really, the arriving of a new race
of people. We should take this seriously. We should take it seriously
because it not only comes from the evidence of tradition, and from
the evidence that comes from the study of cycles, but simply from
what our eyes see as we look about us.

   This world cannot last as it is. At Sherborne we have been talking
about what we should be doing when we finish the present course, and
what people should look forward to in the future. One person gave
an extremely good analogy, which I'm so pleased with that I'd like
to put it to you also. We were talking about the great institutions,
by which the world is at present controlled and dominated – Govern-
ments, great industrial and financial institutions, churches, and international bodies, that have gradually come to dominate the life of
the earth and collected more and more power into their hands. What
is the future of these great institutions? Some have grown very
large indeed – what we call super powers – some have grown into
great international corporations. That there are very large institutions on this earth, there is no doubt. This comparison was made :
but are not these like the dinosaurs that dominated the earth a hundred and eighty million years ago and disappeared from the earth
because they couldn't adapt themselves to the change of climate;
partly because they had no mechanism for maintaining their body
temperature, and partly also because they had very small brains?
One thing that anyone can see on looking at the great institutions of
the world at the present time is that they have very small brains. I
remember many many years ago Ouspensky saying : If you want
to understand the behaviour of nations, you mustn't study animals,

you must study the amoeba. The amoeba knows only one thing – to swallow or be swallowed. It has only one thing, a system that does everything for it; digestion, defecation or perception is all the same thing, it just opens itself to swallow what it can swallow. That is what nations are like. I think that is probably a little bit hard, they have a little more intelligence than that and perhaps we can promote them to the dinosaur level.

Now, one may regard this as a tragedy. Are these beauties to become extinct? Are only their skeletons to be found in a hundred million years? Some people may say – it's about time! What happened when the great reptiles found they were not able to survive was that a new, very humble insignificant form of life appeared – the mammals. They started very small, about the size of mice, I think; but they had one property that the reptiles did not have of being able to regulate their own internal conditions. It was Claude Bernard who said – 'to have a stable inner state is the condition of a free life.' This is the truth about the mammals; because they could maintain in their organism a stable inner state, they were able to survive the great climatic changes that killed off the dinosaurs. It seems that this analogy is very good for prediction and prophecy. Something like the mammals must be among us now, that will, though very small and insignificant, perhaps be destined to inherit the earth. The question is – what is the change of climate that would kill off the big institutions and make their survival impossible? Which are the mammals of the future? What is the destined dominating form of society?

This human world of ours, for a very very long time, has lived on the principle of growth and expansion. This has been particularly noticeable in the last two or three thousand years, but in earlier stages was not so. It has remained not so for certain isolated and, from our point of view, insignificant groups. Until very recently nomads, nomadic shepherds and herdsmen in Central Asia and other places, had no urge to grow. They were quite prepared to remain of one size, and for hundreds, thousands of years, to live in much the same way, moving from place to place. They were not able to be larger because of the limitations of pasturage and so on. And they were superceded. They were even rejected and condemned by the settled people, and very soon after settlement came, the doctrine of growth began to be established in the world. The first really great city in the world was Babylon, where the doctrine of growth was really sanctified. It was the first city by two thousand years to have more than a million inhabitants.

It is an unforgettable thing to visit the ruins of Babylon, stretching thirty or forty miles down the Euphrates, and to see the vast size of this ancient city. Compared with this – and I've visited many many ancient cities – nothing makes the impression of Babylon. Babylon was the first city to live by the doctrine of expansion and growth, and strangely enough, this doctrine was picked up by the Israelites when they were in captivity in Babylon and they even put it into their own sacred books, into Genesis, and even put it in the mouth of God so that it is said that He commanded man to increase and multiply and inherit the earth. It is not a truly Hebrew notion; it is much more a Babylonian notion. But, it has spread throughout the world, and up to our time, two or three thousand years later, growth, expansion, increase, size, quantity, have been the real tests of success, even of virtue and of merit. This is the climate in which we have lived in all this time – that more is better. This 'more is better' creed is really the fundamental creed of mankind – not belief in God, not belief in religion or anything higher. It has brought us to this world in which we live now. It is a dinosaur creed. The bigger you are the better you are. This has now worked itself to saturation. It is no longer possible for mankind to live by this creed.

This is the thing that is going to kill the great institutions, because they cannot live without expansion. Everyone can see this. No occult knowledge is needed to see that as soon as expansion stops, these great bodies get into trouble. Even when expansion is suicide, they have to expand because they know no other way to live. All of us have been so indoctrinated with the belief that more is better, that the more possessions one has, the better one is, that the more one knows, the better one is, the more that one can travel, the better one is. We are so filled with this that any other way of thinking is very hard to adapt ourselves to. We are told, and no doubt it is true, that human knowledge is now doubling every ten years, and that this rate of doubling is increasing. This is regarded as wonderful, also that we are consuming more of the resources of the earth in twenty years than in the whole previous history of the world. I am not sure that it is now regarded as a triumph, because people can see that there are certain flaws in it. But as it becomes impossible – and it is already impossible, and will evidently be impossible, totally and visibly impossible within our lifetime – what will happen to these institutions who live by and only know one thing, and that is the doctrine of more? They will not be able to survive.

How can we turn from this doctrine of more, to a real doctrine of better, from quantity to quality? This is really the difference between the mammals and the dinosaurs. Mammals are much more qualitative. There is much more concern with the quality of life in the mammalian genera than there is in the reptiles. There is a very great doctrine – I think it was Julian Huxley who promulgated it – of being the right size. He wrote a book about it. We should learn from nature that if you want to survive, you must be the right size. A man twenty foot high could not survive, because his surface to volume ratio would be impossible and he couldn't support himself and the rest of it. But this doctrine, this simple doctrine of being the right size, which is beautifully adhered to by mammals, was lost, somehow or other went out of gear, with the great reptiles, the saurians. This has also happened with organizations. Nowadays, no institution thinks of what it means to be the right size. It always wants to be bigger. How are we to look to something else? The whole of this talk up to now is really to lead to this question.

If we say that large institutions are going to fail, it might first seem that the only thing to do is to return to the individual level and save ourselves in the midst of all this. But it is no more true to say that you can go from the great institutions to the individual than to say you can go in search of safety and survival straight from the dinosaur to the amoeba. After all, we as individuals are no more than cells in the life of this world. There has to be something more articulated, more organic, than that; especially in the world as it is today. This obviously leads one to guess that the mammals are small communities, communities that are of the right size. I think that it is as good a guess as there can be, and it is a guess that can be made by people without going through all the analysis I have just given you. People are searching for communities. I had only a few days ago a letter from a publisher of mine in America, who said he wants to distribute a certain book of mine in the United States, especially to communities. He said that there are between one and two million people now, in America, living in small communities, and there was an estimate that there are something like ten thousand communities in different parts of the world, ranging from ten to even a few thousand people. So the search for communities is already in progress. People are experimenting in very very many ways with a new kind of society, in the form of small settlements or communities. But, what is required for this? How are they to survive? How are they to survive if there is a great change in climate? It is one thing to survive as parasites upon another culture, as the early mammals did feed on the carcasses of dinosaurs. But, that kind of thing only lasts for a time.

Communities cannot continue to be parasites upon the great institutions of the world, because these institutions themselves are going to rot away. Can the communities be self supporting? Probably not. But what really is it that is the analogue of the properties that the mammal has, of maintaining the constancy of its interior medium, or the constancy of its own inner world? That is the real question that we must ask ourselves whenever we want to see how a community can live under conditions where they are not sustained by the old law of growth.

It is very easy, if everything is growing and there are surpluses of everything, to live in the atmosphere of surpluses. But supposing it is not so. If we are coming to a time when there will be the forced collapse of growth – and these times are scarcely to be avoided – then those that have power will certainly then seize and hold what they can. It is hardly to be imagined that this world in the next fifteen or twenty years will not go through very severe crises. But how to acquire the kind of self discipline that I think does belong to the future, how to give up the other part of the doctrine of more, and give up the doctrine of power, the wish to dominate? How can one community accept another community, without wishing to dominate it? How can the members of a community be free from the desire to dominate over other members?

Hitherto, the world has been really as much coloured by the doctrine of power as it has by the doctrine of more. If we say that the things that characterise the true society of the future is: the rejection of power and the rejection of more; the acceptance of a mutual need; and the acceptance that the problem, essentially, is to provide what is needed and not what is wanted. These are so easily said, all these things, and everyone is saying them. But, now we're coming to the time when talking about them and wanting them is no longer going to be enough. We are going to be compelled to live this way, or perish, because this is the only way of life that is going to be possible on this earth. All the evidence of history, and I must say, all the evidence that I've had in the fifty years and more that I've seen different kinds of communities in many different countries, all of it convinces me that a community that has no other aim than to survive only holds together so long as there is a threat to its survival. Any community that has no other aim except to provide satisfactory conditions even, fails, because as soon as the conditions are satisfactory, the destructive forces become much stronger than the cohesive ones. But, if we say that communities can only survive under threat, that menace, and menace of loss, of destruction, is the only key to the unity of a community – this is a dismal thought. What is the required thing? I think we here all know this and we must get it clearly into focus.

The only possibility is that there should be a total acceptance of a higher aim than one's own survival, a total acceptance of our need to be related to a higher power than ourselves. In my opinion this has to be freed from its old religious notions, because the religious notions have introduced certain falsification into this. It must be much more direct, much more corresponding to the effects of our actual experience. What is it that regulates? What is it that enables a mammal to maintain this extraordinary state in itself – its constant blood temperature, its constant blood chemistry, its constant tone of its nervous system – so different from that of other forms of life. There is an organic character in a mammal. The life force is organic and it must also be the same way in a community.

One must know and really accept that human nature is not capable of doing this unaided. We must be able to be free from the illusion that man alone can overcome the disruptive forces in his own nature. No community, that is just a human community, ever survives beyond the influence of the pressures that compel it to accept co-operation : as soon as pressure is relieved, disruption begins. This is the human law. It never, to my knowledge, fails of exemplification.

Men will never accept one another, unless they are under some external pressure or threat. It is only when they set their sights beyond humanity altogether, and when they accept that the very purpose of their own existence and of the community which they are

trying to create, and in which they are trying to live, is not survival
– or it is only incidentally survival; it is not human satisfaction –
only incidentally human satisfaction. It is because this is what the
evolution of this earth demands, and because it is demanded, that
the great intelligences that are directing the evolution of the earth,
will help communities that accept this task. This is why it is right
that every community that wishes to survive should look about it
and see what it can do for its environment and not only for itself:
its natural environment and its human environment. But it should
also look beyond that and try to understand – and never be satisfied
with what it already understands, but always try to understand
more and more – the purpose and meaning of life on the earth,
because it is only by serving that purpose that this quality of intrinsic
inner stability can be found that gives you a community that is
really capable of surviving. We must really learn not to trust ourselves, not to trust anything human. We must be disillusioned,
thoroughly disillusioned with man, and learn that we can only put
our trust in a power higher than man. If we can do that, if some
beginnings can come, then these little creatures, these little communities capable of living in the new way, will in the course of time
creep out of their burrows and begin to appear on the surface of
the earth. They will begin to be able to give confidence. People will
see that a new form of life is possible. It will be very very different
from what we know at present, because what I said at the beginning
is also I think essential for this, that there should be new perceptions, going beyond words, new ways of touching one another, and
a new sensitivity towards one another, a new awareness of what
life is and what it requires of us; direct perceptions so that there is
no need to be told. These are the characteristics of the new race,
but these are characteristics that are also inside us, because the
new race will come from us, from our children, or our children's
children. It will not be an ad hoc creation on this earth. It will come
from those who are capable of bearing children that have these qualities, and it will come from us if we set ourselves with real determination to serve the future and to open in ourselves the possibility
of doing so.

*Do you consider that all people at the present have this capacity
to change, or this capacity for evolution, or is it a very gradual
process?*

Yes, we both have it and it's also a very gradual process. Let us take the example of some organ which should be present, and probably will be present in the next race, which is sometimes called the third eye, the higher perception, or the formless perception. The possibility of this exists in all people, but it is mostly so vestigial that it would be very difficult to develop it, and very few would want to or think it necessary to develop these kinds of perceptions. So, in fact it would be very gradual.

Supposing that a fair number of people were to develop another kind of perception, and it became evident that because they had this kind of perception, they were able to understand one another quite differently from the rest of people, this would then perhaps draw many more people to ask – 'Well, can't we do it too?' It is possible to look at it like that, and maybe it could lead to more rapid change; but I still believe, even under those circumstances, that in the present state of the evolution of mankind, which is still fairly early, only a small proportion of people would develop it for a long time to come.

I am simply taking this example so as to give a concrete picture of how someone might look at it. The thing is that people in whom this possibility is rather higher than the average, even markedly higher than the average, even before this has developed in them, do more easily recognise one another and tend, without even knowing how it happens, to be drawn together. This also increases their possibilities; but unfortunately, it also decreases others, because until they are able to convince others that such a possibility exists, they are likely to be looked upon as freaks, or out of place.

*You spoke of these large institutions today having this dinosaur-like quality of 'more is better' and of accelerating increase in size. Couldn't it possibly be postulated that the human race itself has this dinosaur-like quality, tremendous unprecedented increase in population, which doesn't seem to be changing its direction, but accelerating?*

I do not think so. I think that underneath his disruptive and self-seeking impulses, man has deeper ones, and I think that they can be touched and aroused. I do not think that the superficial impulses are really in the nature of man himself. There are people who live contented with what they have, and when they have discovered this secret, they are really the happy people. Maybe this does not answer your question, but I think it should be looked at carefully. Some of you have, no doubt, been in different countries. Were any of you in Nepal before the opening of the road from India? None of you were there. It changed very much recently. Nepal, before there was the road and while it was very little influenced, was a really interesting country. The villagers there were living with very very little, but they were contented. There was no wish for expansion and there wasn't an expansion of population. It is remarkable that whereas India's population was growing by leaps and bounds, the population of Nepal remained pretty stationary. It is a very remarkable thing – if I am right in my facts – that the population of Burma, in spite of everthing, including a fairly good food supply, has remained remarkably stationary. You may say – 'Well, is that something to do with Buddhist countries?' I don't think so. I think it is due to something having remained of this realisation that it is not necessary to have more in order to be happy. You might say – 'Well, Nepal was so poor, that their population couldn't increase and there was no way of getting more.' But I have been in parts of Africa. I remember one large tribe – well, not very large but about five or six villages and about two thousand people altogether – that had migrated to get away from the white people, from South Africa about a hundred years ago, and had gone into a remote valley. There I thought that I saw the happiest people that I had ever seen, living with no urge whatever to get more. That was in 1947 or 1948, just after the war, and the feeling of relief, simply to walk among those people after being among Europeans, is something that I will not forget. I can say that I have seen, myself, essentially stable and old communities in many different parts of the world, certainly in Europe, in some parts of Macedonia, in Asia, in some parts of Africa. I have seen communities that were not dominated by more. You may say – 'Well those are the backward people, those are the people we all despise.' Maybe we've got our picture a little bit upside down. We have so consistently labelled them all as backward, that they themselves are at last beginning to believe in our labels.

*Could you tell us what you understand is the nature of this new type of perception and how it might possibly manifest itself?*

You know that when two people are very close to one another – and it can happen particularly between a man and a woman – that they can come to a point where they know what the other is thinking and find that ideas have occurred to them at the same time as to something that they might do, which they only realise when they speak about it. These ideas have not been communicated in the ordinary way. You know that that kind of thing occurs. That is a kind of perception, that we are all really capable of having and to a much greater degree. But, it is only one kind. Really much more important than the ability of people to communicate with one another without words, is the possibility of communicating where words have in any case no use, and that is with higher levels of being than our own. To be able to do this, and especially to have a two way communication – to know that one can not only be told something, but one can ask, one can explore, to increase one's understanding – to have an awareness that there is a real communication that does not come through the outside, but comes inside, through higher levels of being, is undoubted. There are certainly ways in which these powers of communication can be increased – can be awakened in the first place, and then made to be effective. It is like with a child. First, all it sees is that it sees. Before it is able to recognise forms, a good deal of time has to pass. So it is that sometimes people do have an awakening of these other perceptions, but because there is nothing recognisable, or it takes the form of some ordinary perception, they do not see the importance of what has happened to them and then they do not go on and reach the power to be able to bring it into focus. Without knowing it, they remain like new-born children as far as that particular capacity is concerned. It is there, but they have no idea how to use it, and nobody teaches them, and nobody tells them it is important for them to have it.

*May I ask you about something which I find rather dreadful – that the greatest menace of increase today is increase in world population. That increase in population has been brought about by the implementation of Christian principles; in other words, we have gone to the backward countries and we have introduced hygiene, we have abolished plagues, we have abolished malaria, and a great many of the deadly diseases. We have also to a large extent, and are trying harder than ever, to stop war, which was also a means of keeping the population down. Let us take a really overcrowded part of the world like India, where they are starving. If you and I heard tomorrow, that a terrible plague had broken out there and wiped out a million people, our first thing would be to say – how dreadful. But*

*in our heart of hearts we would really say – how much better off we
all are, because an amount of people have gone and it is better for
mankind. What we are up against, I think, with this increase, is
a whole new value of compassion. Whereas in the past we wanted to
have more people, we wanted to make it easier for more people to
exist, we are getting to the stage when we want them to decrease.
I can't help seeing a great danger that our sense of compassion will
be dulled and a time will come when we say – what a good thing
this catastrophe happened and there are fewer people. What is the
answer to that?*

There is subjective compassion and objective compassion. The subjective compassion, the distress at hearing of suffering, or seeing suffering, and wishing even to alleviate suffering, because it is painful
to us to contemplate it – that kind of compassion doesn't really help
the world, or ourselves, or the object of compassion. There is objective compassion, which is much harder to achieve, and that is a compassion that is able to perceive what is really necessary, possible, and
for the best. It does not mean at all that the best thing is for millions
of people to die of plague, or of some catastrophe, but it may be that
these things will occur, without our wishing it. When one sees in
front of one this suffering of the world – and the suffering of the
world is such that a million people dying is not such a high proportion of the total suffering of the world – it ought to occupy a central
position for us. What should be central for us is the whole present
situation of mankind, which we can perfectly easily see that we are
powerless to change. Not only we, but no human agency at all, can
change it. This I think I did speak of here before. It is necessary to
understand the law that any intentional and conscious change takes
time. The kind of ideas that we have been speaking about here, the
kind of ideas that are important for you here at Beshara, are very
necessary for the world, but they cannot penetrate quickly. Nothing
else but ideas will change the world, but they can only do so at their
own pace, when they become assimilated and people begin to think
differently. That is where the objective compassion comes, that we
should set ourselves to live in such a way that corresponds to what
is best for the world, and that we should be in effect guinea pigs or
demonstration animals to say that it is possible to live in this way,
it is possible to be really happy in this way of living and make these
kinds of sacrifice. It is no easy thing – however much we may say

'Yes, yes' to all this – when it actually comes to giving up having more of something which one has the power to get. It is then the test comes of our objective compassion. This is not because the giving up of eating too much food, or giving up of a certain car, or not driving into London, when we might get in without causing that amount of pollution, that by giving up those things we do something which might lead to a better world; but what is really important is that by having that attitude firmly in ourselves, we become contagious because just as diseases spread by contact, so also does a new point of view spread by contact. We need an epidemic, but that epidemic must be of a new attitude, picked up from people who have it. One has to look objectively. To be distressed over the state of the world, and remain distressed, however distressed one may be, is simply one's own subjective state. It may even be satisfying to us to feel that we are sensitive and able to be distressed and the rest of it. The real thing is to have this objective compassion, to say, 'I must do something myself', that however small in its material consequences, can be very very large in its spiritual consequences.

# Self-Remembering and
# the Transformation of Energies

I have been asked to speak to you about self-remembering in terms of the transformation of energies. Strangely enough I have just been editing Gurdjieff's Third Series* in which he speaks of how groups sprang up after the closing down of the Prieuré, and spread through Europe and America. Gurdjieff said that different people took up bits here and bits there. He said how in one group that were in Russia, they had fastened on to the idea that man has three separate spiritual 'I's', so that each one is required to be separately developed and educated; but another group in Russia fastened on to the idea that the man who doesn't work on himself doesn't have a soul or even a spirit. In a group that was concentrated in Northern Greece, they had picked up the idea of the threefoldness of every cosmic phenomena and concentrated all their interest exclusively on that. But another group in Bavaria had picked up another thing – and he went through various places where people had dispersed to – and then he said that the group that happened to be collected together in England fastened on to the idea that man must remember himself, whereas a group in North America had held on to the idea of self observation and self study and knowing oneself; and how any one single idea produces a breakdown of balance. And he looked round all these places after he had recovered, and began to get in contact with people again, and he saw written across the forehead of one after another 'candidate for the madhouse'. So that although this thing of self remembering and transformation of energies is very important, and it can be said to be one of the forty-nine necessary elements in the all-round development of man, it is only one seventh of one seventh of all that is required, so that if I speak to you about

* Privately printed by E. P. Dutton & Co., Inc., for Triangle Editions, Inc., New York, 1975.

this, you must not forget that it is one seventh of one seventh.

First of all, there are two entirely different processes of transformation of energies. One process depends upon our own initiative and effort, and another depends upon a working from beyond, a working from a higher, more spiritual source, to which we can only respond, so that one can say that among these forty-nine different processes that make up the complete transformation of man, there are one set of processes that are connected with consciousness and awareness, and other sets of processes that are concerned with purification, the elimination of the cancers, and so on. One must know that for the all-round perfecting of man, he has to undergo forty-nine different processes, according to that very sound and balanced tradition.

In the work of self-remembering, there are three energies involved. One energy connected with the body, one with the feelings and one with the thinking power of man. All these are natural energies. They all belong to his human incarnated nature. They are consequences of his being in a body, not just in any animal body, but in a special kind of body, the human body. Truly, self remembering is a state in which these energies are blended with one another and by their blending, they give man an entry into the spirit world, the *'alemi erwah*, or the *'alemi jebberut*; the spirit world, which, you must understand, does not mean spiritual. *Ruh* can translate as spirit or soul and can also mean ghost or apparition. It is only the next world. Sometimes it is called the *'alemi nebati*, the vegetable world; the world of vegetable essences in one terminology. So the first thing to understand is that the self-remembering process is one that belongs to our natural being. It can even be said that man does not even begin to be man until this process is established in him. He is indistinguishable by any kind of cosmic tests from an animal, so long as he does not have this in him. If he were measured by some kind of cosmic scale, it would not be possible to tell by his vibrations that he was not an animal without having in him the state of self remembering. Vibrations of the man that has changed completely become truly human vibrations, *insani*, when he is in this state; so that although he has got in him energies that an animal has not got, until these energies are blended they do not produce from him the kind of vibrations or emanations that are genuinely human.

When we speak of self remembering, we are not speaking about just a mental state. It is not a kind of thought process, though it is a process in one's emotional life. It is not an ecstasy or a state of going out of this world. It is a state in which one is directly and immediately aware that one is a human being, with all the nobility and dignity that belongs to a human being. If you see that this is absent in you, then this must produce in you a state of remorse, or at least a state of regret that you are not the kind of being which you were created to be. But when you begin to be able to be in a state where there is a balance between your body and your feelings and your mental processes, and they are not divorced from one another and there is a blending of these, then you can speak about transformation of energies. Because when energies are blended, then they pass into a different world. Out of the raw material of our quite natural energies; our bodily sensations and the instincts; our feelings and emotions, desires, interests and all our capacity for thought and mental images, we can create something which gives us an entry, a foothold or passport to enter into the next world. If that does not satisfy you, then you must ask some more questions.

*Could you talk a bit about physical food, the relevance of this sort of food?*

As I sit here, you ask questions about the things that I am thinking about. Yesterday I was talking about this subject of food when reading a particular chapter of Gurdjieff's book. I drew attention to this peculiar thing that he says about food, which is very difficult to understand. Food has to undergo a whole series of transformations. It is like the whole evolution, from the vegetable world right up to the human world, and this happens in our own bodies, step by step.

The food is not spiritual nourishment until it has reached our blood and then only when it begins to be blended with the air that we breathe. Until then, food that we eat is not spiritual food, it is simply food for the organism, but when the food has been purified and the coarse and the fine have been separated, and the fine material is now freely dispersed in the blood, then it is able to blend with the energies; with the substances present in the air we breathe. At this point food begins to be spiritual and a certain time comes when it has two paths open to it. At one point it can either evolve further, to become part of the material of our spiritual nature, or it can be transformed into material for excitement, enjoyment and attachment to bind us to this world. The place where this parting of the ways comes is in the cerebellum in the ganglia at the base of the skull. Here we can either become more bound to this world by the food that we eat, or we can take it as the means for liberation. Until then there is not option, it is just an organic process that we need for our physical, organic, psychic life, for the different kinds of experiences that are open to us. But at one point we have the possibility of choosing that some of the substances in the food should not be consumed at once in our psyche, in our experiencing self but that they should go to the supra psychic or higher reason in us. That is the secret connected with food.

Fasting is a sort of symbolic representation of this, not that fasting is not in itself an effective way of bringing about this division, so the food does fulfil all its potential for us, but there is one saying of Mohammed that is very relevant to this. It is one of the *hadiths*, I think, or maybe it was an invented story, who knows? You know that the first convert from the Magian religion, Selman the Persian he was called, became one of the close companions of the Prophet, and he was very highly respected in Persia.

The king of Persia at that time, still possessing very high powers, sent two of his physicians saying, 'You live in these very difficult circumstances down there, with rougher conditions of life than we have, and your mission is very important. I am sending you my two best *tahbibs* to maintain the health and energy of your followers'. So they came down and then after a year they came again to the Prophet and said, 'We've come here, we're all ready to serve, but no one has called on our services. How is it that you never have people getting into trouble? We in Persia, we're always having difficulty with people. We have to adjust their energies and your people don't have to have their energies adjusted.' The Prophet answered 'It's one simple rule we have. Every one of my companions rises from the food while he is still hungry and nobody eats with me until he is satisfied. For this reason we never have any problems with health or with our energies.' The Prophet was very fond of this control of eating. He always fasted more than his own followers. He always had an additional fast over and above the ones that were actually prescribed by religion.

It is not an easy thing to know how to follow this advice. But if we learn to ask our own inner self to watch over this for us, we begin to develop a certain kind of sensitivity that can tell us at any moment whether it is the right moment to stop eating, and having eaten, what kind of activity is appropriate, so that the energy that comes from the food will all go to the right place; whether it is desirable to be very active and exert the physical body or whether it is necessary to be still and quiet. This inner knowledge has to be acquired and is not subject to rules. It is not really possible to say to people – everyone should eat so much, or everyone should, after eating, have a time of rest, or that everyone after eating should have a time of intense physical activity, because the balances of energies in people are different. But everyone really has this place at the base of the skull which is the parting of the ways. If we begin to become sensitive to this and know when we can allow our energies to flow outwards and when we have to direct them inwards, then we can keep a balance between outward activity, which is the fulfilment of our duties as incarnated beings and the inward activity which is the perfection of our own nature and our path of liberation, our path out of this world and preparation for our further destiny after this life. The balance point for all this is at the base of the skull.

*If it is all here and now, one of the great problems, it seems to me, with people aspiring on this path is that as it is all here and now, what do we do about coming to grips with the concept of the next life or the world to come?*

It depends how firmly established we are. For one who is firmly established, the past and the future are seen to be *khayal*, seen to be a dream. They are not concerned with it. They know that everything is here now, and everything is already what it is for them, but to be firmly established, *mutma'in*, that is for those who are so. It is no use to anyone to pretend to himself, to say that – I have now set myself to live without concern for the past or future, because for this you have to be liberated from fear, from desire, from the craving for existence. If one is, one is. If one is not, one cannot pretend it.

Now, what is the stage of those who have not come to this established state? For them the past and the future are not illusion, because they belong to the world in which there is a past and a future. If you were in a world which is subject to time, it means that you yourself are subject to time, you have to live in that way. First of all, for example, we are incarnated beings. This incarnated state of being in a body makes it inevitable. We have to be connected with time.

When I was asked to come down and talk with you, I had to find out if there was something else that I should be doing at this time, but as this body of mine is not capable of doing what my inner can perhaps do, and that is both to be here talking to you and also up at Sherborne talking to another lot of people, I had to find out whether I had to be talking to somebody else before coming to talk to you. That is one of the limitations of being incarnated in a body, and the same is true also about our psyche. The psyche of man, his personal identity, also is a time-like state, and it is no use thinking that this personal identity of ours can have the freedom that belongs to the completely liberated. Though we can say that there are three different things at least that have to be taken into account. First of all there is the incarnated state of being in a body. Then there is the state of the psyche, of the life of the conscious experience of man; one cannot not take that into account. For this incarnated being, there is a process, a death, which is the separation from this physical body and the end of the physical body's spiritual life. It then becomes a thing, like other things, and again its elements merge into the planet from which it came. The second part of man is still, even when it is separated from the body, subject to time, then there is a problem; one can speak of after death, and after life, only one must really clearly know that this is only because one is held by that kind of existence, a psychic existence. Let that dissolve, let that go, let that no longer hold us – then there is no question of future and no concern, no after life, nor is there an after or before. However, it is no use for us to say that because our goal is to come to this timeless freedom or state of unity, we must therefore live our lives as though it were the situation now, for we are not free. This applies, not merely to this physical body and this condition here, but also to our psychic nature, which is not able to be free. That which can be free from time, past and future, is beyond, it is the Divine nature in us.

It looks like a paradox at first, to say that the reality is timeless and thus is here and now, therefore let us only concern ourselves with this. But, no, for we are so created that we are also in-time-like creatures. This has been done to us and is not our choosing. Maybe it was our choosing, but nobody can really put himself back to the moment of his creation and ask whether it was given to him to choose or to obey. But whatever it is, here we are, in this state of affairs, which does include part of us which is not tied to or not wholly dependent upon this physical body. The second part of us

must learn how to liberate itself, to be able to be free from the physical world, but that does not mean that it is free from time, but that
it is free from all the limitations.

I am giving you a simplified version when I say there is an incarnated material state, a psychic or discarnated, but yet temporal
state, and a state of liberation, when there is no body, no psyche, no
time, no past, therefore no future, no dependence on anything, no
difference between one and many, and therefore no difference between God and creature. Although it is true that the latter state is
also there, we are placed in such a situation that we have to work,
if we have it in us; and if this is our destiny, we shall do so to return
to this state of pure freedom, as free as God.

*What is the function of 'the misleader'?*

Why is it that an animal cannot achieve the liberation we speak
of, so long as it remains in this state of existence? You see the answer
of that. Is it because an animal cannot be tempted; cannot be mis-
led? This has been given to us, to give us the possibility that we
should be transformed from our human state, but also that we can
become less than an animal, which is the price for our being able to
become more than human. When the world was created with order,
then it was seen that this world could never fulfil its purpose, and
so disorder was inserted into it.

*I didn't follow you when you said 'less than an animal', because
when one is being tempted, very frequently one doesn't know that
this is happening. Is this actually the state of being less than an
animal?*

This is why I said at the very beginning, in answer to the first
question about remembering oneself, ('What is the purpose of self
remembering?'). It is that which enables us to discern the spirits. I
think St. James puts it that this discernment cannot come in the state
of animal consciousness. It is possible for us to have such a blending
of our states, that we can be sensitive and discern and recognise;
this is the beginning, but if there were not this *wiswas* – one of the
most beautiful Arabic words – because you see it's not. It's not as if
we had a clear thing put in front of us – here's this apple. You eat
this – you know God has told you not to, but you eat it. If it were
all as clear as that! But this is not how it works. It is *wiswas*. Do you
know that *sura* – it is one of the very short *suras* at the end of the
arrangement of the Koran by length of *suras*. It's very interesting

how this goes because you ask to have discernment against this spirit of confusion and doubt as it manifests itself in the genii and in men, in the invisible forces that act within us and also in the behaviour of people. It's one of the recommended *suras* for recitation, because it is, I suppose, a short one which you recite before the *Namaz*.

*Could you say something about the nature of faith?*

Every question that you've asked me today, I've been asked in the last forty-eight hours. In fact the question I was asked was about hope. Hope is the growing awareness that the creative power is benevolent. You reflect on that, meditate on that. This is our hope. If it were indifferent to us or if it were hostile to us, then there would be no hope.

Faith – I say this about it. The first thing really is to grasp what I've said about hope, that this process of our own transformation is not being done in an indifferent environment, and certainly not in a hostile one. But that doesn't mean that there isn't hostility. Of course there is. But the great thing is that the creative power is concerned with our own creation, which is now in process at this very moment. It is not a matter of cosmic indifference that you and I can become divine beings. As we hold on to that, then we begin to understand one other saying, which I think is a *hadith*, which is that 'Who comes one step towards Me, to him I come ten steps.' As that begins to work in you, you begin to experience and see for yourself how much more comes to you than you give, how the fruits of your own puny sacrifices are so much beyond what you could possibly be entitled to in a moment of sincerity. Then this comes round to something else. Your inward fears begin to evaporate from this, your sense of insecurity – that all comes from the profound and right awareness that you are nothing, that you have nothing that can stand up to this deceptive spirit, to the forces that there are in this world, and yet you know that there is something there, and this knowledge, this awareness, actual awareness begins to grow in you. It changes, then, from being an awareness that the creative power is benevolent, favourable to us, to an awareness that the creative power is actually working in us. Then this begins to be faith.

*How is a person a channel for healing?*

You remember, I said that of the forty-nine different things that have to work in order to achieve completion and perfection of man, that some of them depend upon us, our positive action. Some depend upon our own initiative. Some depend upon our readiness to make sacrifices, to abandon, to give up. Others, again, depend simply upon our being able to accept and respond, and since all of these are necessary, any way that confines itself to one of them – that says that the great healing power will do all the work, all you have to do is to respond to it – you've said one of the forty-nine truths, but you've not said the other forty-eight. If you say – we've got to remember ourselves – man must do this because it is in his power to, and he's got to set himself to be attentive and alert, *mindful* – the Buddha puts it, and you've said one of the forty-nine truths and if you say – this is the only truth, you're only about two per cent right. If you say – there is a healing power that will also purify us at the same time, this is true but it is only true if it is combined with many other things as well. It always turns out to be like that. If you say – what happens? How is a person a channel for healing? The truth is that there are a whole range of healing energies that work in different ways. There are healing energies that simply release the energies that are in the organism itself and enable it to do its own healing. There are other paramount energies that work directly and almost instantaneously – miracle working that is – although, if you talk about healing, you must understand you are talking about a variety of things, and there is healing that requires the assent and the faith of the person who is going to receive this action. There are others where he cannot know, and even be hostile and reject the whole thing, and yet the action will happen in him. Know all these things. Experience tells that there are all these different varieties of healing action. But there is a healing action that carries with it a purifying, but that particular one does require a certain state of consent, and this I've noticed for myself – if that particular action is invoked without an unreserved acceptance of the need to sacrifice one's own faults and weaknesses – self-love and egoism and so on – if there isn't this, then that healing may work, but the result is very bad, because the result then comes back on the head of the person, so that it is very very dangerous to submit oneself or to participate in healing activities unless one knows which kind it is and whether – if it is a certain kind of healing – whether the people themselves are in the right state. If it is another kind of healing, it doesn't matter whether they are in the right state or not. It's a good thing, this thing that I've said to you about this forty-nine. It's seven times seven. And even if you don't know them, it is a very great safeguard for one to remember – I know this, and I know that these things are good, but how many things are there that I don't know? And how many things, therefore, have I got simply to pray for? Where we don't know, there's nothing left to us except prayer. When we know, we can act. When we don't know, we have to pray. Therefore, always we have to say – what I know, I will do. What is working in me, I will encourage and I will help. All that I don't know, all that I'm not able to respond to because of my ignorance – let that happen as it should in me, in spite of my ignorance; some prayer like that is needed.

# The Seven Lines of Work

*To what extent can we learn from one another?*

Our relationship with God becomes a direct one, only when a certain degree of purity is reached. If we speak in terms of *fana* and *baqa*, it is not after the first *fana* that one already arises to the awareness of our relationship with God. God still remains hidden from us. Therefore, we have to realise that this is a journey, a pilgrimage. The question is whether we can make this pilgrimage alone, or whether it is better made in the company of others; and if so, why? There are so many things to say about this, that I had to take a good time to try and get it into focus for myself.

First of all, as you said, we can't see ourselves very easily. There is a *hadith* – 'Be ye mirrors to one another' – and this seeing oneself in others is prescribed as a 'way' in all religions, many sides of which are expressed in picture form. For example, in the *Conference of the Birds*, they needed one another. Various explanations of this kind can be given, but I would have said that there is another way which is immediate. I can say how it is for me – I never doubt my need for other people. I remember long ago saying this, and somebody said to me: 'Yes, but you have groups and you have people to work with – of course it's like this, but supposing you had no groups and no people to work with, then what would you do?' And I said: 'Well, I'd go out into the street and grab the first person I met,' because I've never had the feeling that I could do it alone without the fellowship of other people. When I thought of answering your question I thought, 'Well, the answer is that no explanation is needed – surely it is obvious to us all that we need one another, and that we should also remember (and this is a thing I wanted specially to say about this) that we are not, after all, special in God's eyes.' We may seem to be special any way you like, but we are not special for God. I was talking about this at Sherborne on Tuesday, which was St. George's Day – we were having the feast on that occasion – and speaking about the necessity of being free from any feeling of being special.

If one says – 'I will find my own way to God', it is terribly difficult not to feel oneself to be different from other people. I have spoken about this before, but for me it is so important that I always have to bring it up if it arises. It's much more important that we are human beings, than that we are this particular human being. To feel oneself as ordinary is the one safeguard against many different enemies that come from our own egoism. Anyone who really feels that he or she is ordinary, and really does genuinely feel it, is protected from many enemies. One way of feeling ordinary is really to be aware that we are all in the same boat.

You see, we speak about our relationship to God. Of course, this should be the strongest motive over all other motives. But look, for example, at the Christian Beatitudes with which the Sermon on the Mount begins. It is the fifth which says 'Blessed are the pure in heart, for they shall see God', it is not the one with which it starts. Much has to happen first. It starts off with 'Blessed are the poor in spirit, for theirs is the Kingdom of Heaven.' This means : blessed are those who aren't carrying about any ideas of themselves that they are something. That is just what I'm saying, that blessed are ordinary people, who feel themselves to be ordinary, they are the significant ones. Then the next Beatitude is that you have to pay the price of suffering – 'Blessed are they that mourn' – and you've got to be ready to go through that, and accept it as a necessity on the way. Then – 'Blessed are the meek' – this means something very important, which is 'Don't attempt to do anything by force', and speaks about those who are free from violence. This is why it said 'Blessed are the meek, for they shall inherit the Earth.' This Beatitude really should be understood, and has an enormous importance for our time, when everything is tried to be done by force and by power and by violence. Always people are surprised when they read this – why should the meek be the ones to inherit the Earth? The answer is because it is the only way in which this Earth can become a spiritual home for man. As long as the violent, or the power-possessing and the power-exercising people are in control, it cannot be.

Then comes: 'Blessed are they that hunger and thirst after righteousness, for they shall be filled.' This means that there has to be this very strong aspiration, just to have one's being right, to be free from the negative things, and to have the necessary strength. Then comes our attitude towards other people – 'Blessed are the merciful, for mercy shall be shown to them.' A very important and very strange thing about this Beatitude is that it's the only one where what you receive and what you give are the same. It coincides, really, if you look at it, with that *hadith* of the Holy Prophet – 'Be ye mirrors to one another' – it is really where what we were talking about comes in. And then, when those four conditions have been fulfilled, there comes the purity of heart which gives one a direct consciousness of the presence of God. That is how it's presented there in these Beatitudes. From that comes manifestation – 'Blessed are the peacemakers' – when from the presence of God, it is possible to manifest. Manifest for what purpose? – to make peace.

The Beatitudes are a very marvellous picture of the pilgrimage. In them is the answer to all the questions that you are putting. From this point of view, the aim, the final objective, is not to see God. Having seen God, the aim is to be able to make peace and bring peace to mankind. Finally comes the last bit about conscious labour and intentional suffering – 'Blessed are they which are persecuted for righteousness sake, for theirs is the kingdom of Heaven' – the whole thing comes round to the beginning. This and the first Beatitude both refer to what kind of people are those of the kingdom of Heaven. You can't pick out any one of the Beatitudes and say – that's the one I'm going to live by, and not the others.

*Is it necessary to study various writings in this work or is too much emphasis placed on this?*

You see, when knowledge and being become one, it is different. It is what is called the *'alemi imkan*, the third world. Then it is not necessary to know because one is known. However, this is the third stage. Much has to be done before that world is reached.

There has to be a mental image of the path. Certainly, the less that one has to rely on words, the better; but, it still has to start this way, and better than words are pictures, better than pictures are experiences, better than experiences is direct perception. But, again, there is a path to follow.

You see, we have a very distorted idea of the world, not only in how we think about the world, but in what is actually built in behind our thinking which we are not even aware of. We need to have a re-furnishing – one cannot get away from it. Our method of education and our whole educational system is almost exclusively directed towards the material world, or to the world of bodies – the *'alemi edjsam*, the tangible world, the world of separation – which one has to know about, because otherwise one can't participate because one cannot enter it directly. So much has been done to us from birth to make us take this world as the reality, that something has to be done to develop new modes of thought. This really matters. I might come here to do nothing else except give you particular techniques for doing this or that, opening this or that door of perception, but in fact I come and talk about such things as you ask me about at the beginning. Only, this kind of study should be presented in the way that, for example, *Ibn 'Arabi* does, of giving many pictures. He does most of it by means of pictures and not very much by means of abstract presentation. You should set yourselves to connect the first two stages – I mean, the first stage of presenting ideas in the form of words and the second of presenting them in the form of pictures – and then connect them further with one's own experience, so that it becomes quite natural to search in one's own experience for illustrations, even of very lofty ideas; because everything, however deep, can also be understood simply. If you tell me of an idea that people find difficult to approach, that they feel is either too abstract, or not sufficiently connected with the problem of daily life or the problem of working on oneself and strengthening one's own being, then I'm sure I can show you that there is a connection. Have you anything, any abstract ideas that you feel difficult to connect with your own immediate experience?

*If we're going to talk about Ibn 'Arabi, then the a*'yan al thabitah – *How does one connect that?*

Let me just put a question to you. Supposing that somebody were to offer you ten thousand a year to go off and run some splendid business, and on one condition, that you'd never think of these kind of ideas again, what would you do?

*I wouldn't be able to do it.*

Well, that's the *a'yan al thabitah*. Because you know in yourself that you wouldn't be able to do it. That unshakeable awareness that you could not abandon – that is the *a'yan al thabitah*. Mind you, it can open up to much more, but that is fundamentally what it means. It is in the Sermon on the Mount also – 'No man can serve two masters, but either he will flee to the one, and despise the other, or he will love the one, and hate the other.' It is put like that. It is a picture. You can come to realise that there is something in you that you could not abandon, whatever was offered to you, and at the same time you may be fully aware that if you really serve this for five minutes in the day, you are doing well : you are aware how little you do about it, and yet you cannot stop. Do you understand?

I remember when such an offer was made to me shortly after the war. I was invited to go down to South Wales, with the possibility of eventually becoming the chief executive of one of the biggest industrial groups in England, and I knew that if I took this on, it would mean giving myself; and the board of directors who offered it to me also knew that I had to make that choice. I either had to serve that, and really serve it – or not – and I remember how simple it was.

*Could you tell us something more about service?*

I've spoken to you about the seven lines of work, haven't I? The work concerns within and without, and there is also in this an active state and a receptive state. There is one kind of work, which consists in our active searching for what we need – that's where we're active in order to get something from without. Study properly belongs to that line. It can be called search, but it's more than search, because it is really taking in and assimilating by one's own activity and intention. It is this first line of work that drives one to seek a teacher, a source. It begins perhaps, by reading. There are quite a variety of things that belong to this, but they're all characterised by our active striving to get the help we need : the mental food, the spiritual food that we need, from those who have it; or in some cases from nature.

The second kind of work is that which goes on inside us. It is the action between one part of our nature and another. This we call inner work. When seek to overcome in ourselves, ill-will and grasp-ingness, self-love and so on, this is the struggle of one part of us with another; a very necessary work. This is where the work is very often painful. It involves, perhaps, self denial. In fact, in some form or another, it is always self denial, because one part of us affirms against another one that rejects. That work on oneself, or inner work, has, as you can see, many different aspects.

The third is where the work is from the inside to the outside. This is service, where we give from what we have. This is also necessary for us, and there cannot be self-perfecting without service. The principle of service is always, and in everything, to give more than we take and to use our own powers to contribute to the spiritual progress of the world, from ourselves and from what we are able to do with such means as we possess. That is the third line of work.

The fourth line I leave for the moment because it's a special thing that comes up at the end. In each case the lines I have described depend upon something active on our part. We have to go out and search – 'seek knowledge, even in China,' the Holy Prophet said. Then there is this struggle with oneself, where we have to be active towards ourselves, not let ourselves be weak and lazy and self-indulgent, or self-loving, or ill-willful. And there is the active work to help others, to serve the world and to serve nature.

Then comes the fifth line, where we have to be receptive. This is exemplified in the *salik* who goes to the teacher and says 'Will you teach me?' and the teacher says 'Will you let yourself be taught?' To be receptive, to allow oneself to be helped, is not so easy; that is, to know when to do nothing from oneself, to allow oneself to be directed, to allow oneself to be shown. The need here is for trust, for acceptance. This enables something to be given to us, that we couldn't take for ourselves. Gurdjieff has a very pretty story to describe this, about what he calls the squirming idiot. He says that he is like a fish out of water. A fish is on the side of the bank and can't get back, and it knows that if it doesn't get back into the water, it will die. And a compassionate man goes by and wants to save this fish, and he picks the fish up, but the fish wriggles out of his hands, and he can't put him back, and he tries and he cannot, until the fish is too far gone to be helped. To be able to be quiet enough, to be able to be receptive enough, to allow ourselves to be helped is also a work, and for some people it is a particularly difficult line to follow. It is also part of group work, so that when one is in a group, one does accept to really be part of the group. I think that what I said at the beginning about not being special also enters into this. To be able to abandon the idea that one is special opens many doors that one can never open by any activity or by any force of one's own. That belongs to the fifth line.

The sixth line is from within. It is the really spiritual action. This is the core of meditation. Really the essence of meditation is to allow oneself to be taken by the spirit into a different state. It is different. This is not help coming from outside. It is wholly within. In this sense there is no one else but oneself and the spirit, or the light of the spirit, you can call it, or whatever words you like to use for this. What matters is to learn to give oneself to the spirit and to put one-self aside. It is said –'resist not the spirit'. This kind of inner respon-siveness, really to know how to let oneself go under a spiritual action and to put aside any idea of doing anything oneself belongs to the sixth line.

The seventh is the line of grace, of action that has no 'why?' to it. Something comes to us that we haven't earned, that we couldn't have brought about by ourselves, that we haven't even prepared ourselves for, and a door is opened. This seventh is necessary – with-out this there would be no chance for us, because there are some things that cannot possibly be earned. This is the Divine action in the soul. As far as this action is concerned, every part of us is without – therefore it is really an action from within to without – from God to the soul, in this case. This happens even without our wish, even sometimes against our wish. Sometimes things happen to us that we regard as misfortunes, that we would wish had not happened; and then later we see that this was the one blessing that made something possible for us, and we become thankful, but not at the time of its happening. This is why it is very different from the sixth line – as in the sixth line, our own responsiveness, our own opening ourselves inwardly is required.

Meditation doesn't force itself upon us, doesn't overcome our will, but grace does. It shows itself in the very simplest thing of all, and that is when thoughts such as remembering the reason of life comes into us, quite unbidden. There we are thinking quite different kinds of thoughts, and then something reminds us; suddenly we remember that this is not what we're here for. Such a very simple change of state inside ourselves, that we know is not earned, and couldn't be earned, because we were not in a position, not in a state where we could earn it – we were lost in dreams, or in some state, some emo-tional state maybe – gives us the chance of looking at things differ-ently. All of that, from the simplest to the most profound, all that kind of gratuitous action, the grace of God, belongs to the seventh line. And it's true that without this, there would be no other line. Everything starts really from this.

Now what is the fourth line, which I've left to last? In the fourth line, we're neither active nor passive. It is manifestation. It is when it passes through us, when we can use all our powers, but we are not using them in our own name. That is why it's different from service. Manifestation is, really and truly, a state of possession. The spirit takes possession and what we say and do is not ours. We are neither active nor passive. In the simplest forms it is when we have to play some role. For example, I am now playing the role of teaching you – but I am not entitled to teach you, nor do I teach you from myself. What I am telling you didn't come from me. It happens that it didn't come from any person. Some time ago, when I was talking one day, all this came – it was manifestation of a spiritual power or a spiritual presence. This comes whenever we have to fulfil a role, and don't attempt to do anything, when we're neither active nor passive, but just go with it. This is best expressed in *Tao*. The wise men of old didn't do anything, neither actively nor passively, and yet by their presence everything was done – the presence of one such man would ensure the welfare of a State, and so on. This is a high, high way of looking at manifestation, but we also have to do it in a simple way : when we are in front of some role to be played, and we're not concerned with ourselves, and don't imagine that it's we who are doing anything. I am playing at this moment the role of teaching you and you are playing the role of listener. Your role is just as important and just as necessary.

All of these lines are important. It is not possible to have a balanced life unless all of them are present in us. When they're all present, it is the right state. If you ask how much time should be spent in one line and how much time should be in another, that's not so easy a question to answer, you know. The true inner work is timeless. It's only the preparation for it that takes time.

# Meditation and Will

*When you were talking about the stages of relaxation, you talked only about the first three, and I was wondering, in connection with learning how to sleep properly, if it was connected with these stages of relaxation, and what is involved in learning how to sleep properly.*

What happens when you are not sleeping? Do you have your mind simply running on the day?

*Lying in bed, I've been trying to relax and then working on my breathing; awareness of breathing, watching it, and I began to notice that even when a certain kind of stillness comes and the mind isn't going round and round, that only the awareness of breathing is keeping me awake.*

It's a very strange thing about sleep that trying to put oneself to sleep wakes one up. What about trying the other way, trying to wake yourself up? If you get into the state when all sorts of little wheels are turning in you, thoughts turning round and round, and if you are occupied, as you say, with breathing and trying to become yourself relaxed, if you really look at this state, you can see that this would not be expected to put you to sleep. Supposing that you take a *Zikr* and set yourself to do this *Zikr* very sincerely, the *ism-i-azam*, let us say, and you repeat the *Zikr* to yourself and try to keep your attention on it, try to get as much meaning out of it as you can. This, I can tell you from my own experience, always puts me to sleep. I try to see if I can do the *Zikr* for a quarter of an hour without going to sleep and I never succeed. If I try to put myself to sleep within a quarter of an hour, two hours later I shall still be awake.

This has to do with energies. You have a certain active energy in you, and you try to bypass it; you try to get to a state of relaxation where this active energy will not be disturbing you, but it is still there. Therefore, this active energy has to be put to positive use. It will sometimes even bring you further, because the time between waking and sleeping, especially in the middle of the night, is a time when we are closer to the *'alemi erwah* – the spirit world – and we can receive illuminations from it. So it is possible to say to oneself, 'As I am not sleeping, or as I am not able to sleep now, I will put this time to profit; I will do this *Zikr*, calling on the name of God, and asking that I should be shown something which will be useful to me.' Then, in my experience, either of two things happens. Either I do go off to sleep, or something useful is shown to me. The *Zikr* does not need to be in Arabic. You can repeat the Lord's Prayer, or you can repeat any invocation, anything which invokes the name of God. *Allah Hu*, or simply *Allah;* or 'Jesus Christ, Son of God, have mercy on me,' or anything. They all have the same intention, to turn ourselves towards God and to open ourselves to receive whatever gift God chooses to give us, and He may give us the gift of sleep. When you are relaxing, this liberates you from your body, in order to be active. You do not really relax in order to be passive. The highest state of relaxation is *fana-i-af'al*, that is, the abandonment of the notion that one is oneself the agent. Then comes the *fana-i-sifât*, and then the *fana-i-dhât*, which is the last, the sixth; and then the final and last stage of relaxation is that of the *Hu*, of the *huwiyet*, of the final Unity. So the higher stages are still relaxation, if you understand the word *fana* : *fana* is relaxation, is letting go.

If I use a word like *fana*, and it's not clear to you, stop me and say 'What do you mean by *fana?*', and I will explain to you, both in the conventional way and also what I understand by it. First of all, *fana* means the passing into non-existence or the disappearance or dissolution, and *baqa* is the resurrection or the renewal and re-establishment. It is said that the progress of the soul is from *fana* to *baqa;* to a fresh, higher *fana* and so on. It is surrender, or abandonment. 'Letting go' is probably a good English rendering, if you understand how very much the words 'letting go' can mean. Now, if we say *fana-i-af'al*, *af'al* is the plural of the Arabic word *fi'l* which means doing or action. It is letting go of action. Non-attachment is a way of translating this. But it means something special in Sufism. It means letting go of the illusion that I am the doer, understanding that I am the receptive principle, that God is the doer; that He is active, I am responsive. I give up the idea that I am the active one and I cease to be attached to action.

In the Hindu, in the *Gita*, this is really the oldest *yoga*. Non-attachment is in one of the early chapters of the *Gita*. They call it inaction in action, action in inaction, and so on. All of this represents a very great step, and it is the first true *fana*. He who has been able to pass through this *fana*, comes directly under the Will of God. His life is not separated, and therefore he enters what is called the *'Alemi imkan*. *'Alem* means world, that is the world which is directly subject to the Will of God, the world of surrender, *taslim*. It is in that that we can prepare ourselves for Unity, for the surrender of our own being, not only of our own actions. All that is implied in this word *fana-i-af'al*, and this represents a great step. Before that, there is something else, that is, the state of disillusionment with the world, which is called *fana-i-ahkam*, where you become aware that this material world, this visible world, cannot give you what you need, where you cease to put your trust in it and you cease to identify your own existence with possessions, with achievements, with the opinion of the world. All that is possible, that *fana-i-ahkam*. Ceasing to rely on this visible world, without having really changed one's own nature, which is why it's called a false *fana*. It is simply a change in one's values and attitudes. The first real *fana* is something much deeper, because instead of ceasing to rely upon the world, and upon being supported by the world, one ceases to rely upon oneself and one doesn't feel that it's important that *I* should be the doer, and one is able to surrender this need to be something. One accepts that one is a recipient and that it is the Divine Grace that makes one anything. This change is a very big change.

*Ibn-'Arabi describes two mystical states. He describes eight and he divides them into two. I thought it was* fana *and* baqa, *and I thought he said that* fana *was a state where one was not conscious of anything, whereas* baqa *was a state where one was fully conscious, as if, in* fana, *one withdrew. He talks about complete passing away of the self. . . .*

I think *Ibn 'Arabi* recognises different degrees of *fana*, which I've been speaking about. *Fana* and *baqa* can be translated as 'death' and 'life', *fana* being 'death' and *baqa* being 'life'. *Baqa* means to be existent and *fana* means non-existent, but this is really our own state. To be aware of one's nothingness is not to be unconscious. He never speaks of *fana* as a state of unconsciousness.

*Could you say something further about the stages of relaxation?*

If you like, instead of my explaining it and describing it in words, we can do it.

Before one begins anything, one should invoke the name of God. I shall say no more than *Bismillah er Rahman er Rahim*. You understand that in saying that, or something of this kind, one is acknowledging that one is not acting in one's own name, but in the name of God, the Compassionate, the Merciful. I am not doing what I am doing by my authority, but in His name. We have an instrument that is given to us, and this instrument makes us *Wakil*; that is, representative of God. We are entrusted with a certain power, to act upon this material world and to rule it, not only the dead but the living. This power is that of voluntary attention, the power of directing a certain creative energy by our own will. This is something that is not given to the animals. So, after having invoked the name of God and placed ourselves inwardly in this attitude, that we are not the doer, but God is the doer; that we are not the authority, that it is in the name of God that we act, we then have to have the courage, not only to act in God's name, but act as God does.

This, 'Be, and it was', this is the Creative Word in the Koran. It is with this Word that we bring about the states in ourselves that we need. Now, because the parts of our body that are concerned with the maintenance of the rhythm of life have their own direction in us, we should not interfere with these organs until it is revealed to us how they work and what they need. For this reason we work with other parts of the body; the organs by which we work on the outer world, in particular our four limbs. This is why so many spiritual exercises are directed in and through the arms and legs. If we can relax our arms and legs sufficiently deeply, they will draw the tensions out from the other organs where we should not yet act directly. So, we bring our attention with the command to relax. In the first place we have to give this command to the muscles of our body. This we can do very simply. For example, if we clench our right hand, we can just as easily tell it to relax. It will do so because the order is carried by our attention. And so we go on.

*Should one be concerned about falling asleep in meditation?*

There is no harm in falling asleep in meditation. I seriously say to you, never mind about falling asleep in meditation. It may be that you have entered the *'alemi erwah*. It is possible that you can really enter the spirit world in this way. This condition, which the Hindus called *Sushupti*, is a very desirable one. That which happens to us in meditation does not depend upon our consciousness. It is deeper than consciousness, and therefore there is not the slightest need to struggle to be conscious or to remain conscious, but one does the meditation. Is it with a *mantram* or in what form do you meditate?

*Not with a mantram.*

It may be desirable to take something more specific into it, because you may fall simply into ordinary sleep. But still I say to you, even if you fall into ordinary sleep and not into *Sushupti*, it is still quite compatible with the meditation. You should always start the meditation with an act of intention. You do that, don't you?

*We have a dedication.*

I say to you that one must not be anxious about this, because the sleep is not lost. The action from the meditation, the spiritual action, is beyond consciousness. It is quite true that if one's posture is right, it very often happens that there is a hiatus, where there is a cessation of consciousness and one does not know how long this cessation has lasted. This is the real thing that happens: you may sometimes feel that you have been asleep for a long time, or unconscious for a long time, and it is only a moment. One of *Ibn Arabi's* stories about *Khidr* demostrates this change. You go out of time and a whole eternity of events may occur, and yet you discover that it was only a moment before that your head was plunged in the water. I was particularly thinking of this break of consciousness where, for a time you cannot measure yourself, because you lose all contact with time. You have been unconscious. This sometimes passes over into sleep and one doesn't wake up for some minutes, but I think that probably on the whole it would be advisable to have a *Zikr* or *mantram* or something or other, simply to be a vehicle that will keep one's attention. Nevertheless, if this does pass into sleep, it really does not lose anything. About falling over – do you sit crosslegged or on your heels?

*We use meditation stools.*

I think that the meditation stool is all right until your muscles become sufficiently relaxed, but I could not understand how you did fall over, but now I see. People do sometimes like to use some kind of stool. I do not stop them when I see that they have gone off and made themselves a little stool or something, but it is not really necessary. One can become perfectly comfortable by just sitting on one's heels, although there are certain people who have some awkwardness, or something which makes it difficult for them. But about the meditation stool, some people claim, 'Oh, but this helps me to stay awake, when I'm frightened of falling off, it keeps me awake.' That is the worst thing; You are not giving youself to the meditation. With meditation there should be complete *taslim*, complete surrender of oneself, *tawakkul*. It means to put the responsibility on to God. *Wakil*, you know, means a representative or an agent, and *tawakkul* means to dedicate to somebody, dedicating to God. This is the whole point of meditation, to allow God's power to work in us. If part of our attention has to be given to keeping our balance, then we are not really giving this a chance. I have, for example, – and probably many of you have – practised the transcendental meditation of the Maharishi Mahesh Yogi. There he does not think anything of attitude. You can sit in any kind of comfortable seat and do just as you like. I myself think that is exaggerating. There were a large number of people meditating at a meeting in Rome, and half of them were fast asleep. I thought that was overdoing it, because they were all sitting in comfortable armchairs with their feet up.

When I meditated with *dervishes* in Asia, there they had that attitude of clasping one knee. But it is not a wise thing, in my opinion, to take a posture in meditation that requires attention, that takes part of one's attention to maintain it. The *yogis* have a nice stable and easy posture, and this is the lotus posture, with both feet crossed one over the other. I say stable and easy – stable and easy for me thirty years ago, that is!

*Could you tell us something about Khidr?*

I would be rather careful how I talk about Khidr. This entirely depends upon Khidr. I would not talk about him behind his back. If he gave me permission to talk about him, I would talk.

*Sometimes, like yesterday, I really did not want to go to meditation, I felt that it was not the right thing for me to be doing, and as it was I ended, for most of the meditation, by becoming more and more insane inside. Now, in a case like that, so often one's own judgment is wrong and it comes from the wrong motivation. Should you give up that desire not to do something, or should one follow that feeling?*

I remember Pat Terry Thomas, when she was with the *Shiva Puri Baba*, asked him, 'How are we to know whether what moves us is our own will or God's Will?' He said, 'Always own will – no difficulty. Never think it is God's Will.' The point is that God's Will can move you only when you're just precisely not thinking that. This question is about whether one should bring oneself to a certain action that one is unwilling to do. This is totally different according to the kind of action it is. For one's duty, one must make oneself go, whatever state one may be in. Meditation should not have anything forced in it. If I say something more, you must understand that this is my own advice, this is not universal advice. I say to people at Sherborne that there is one thing in the day towards which you are totally free and you need have no sense of obligation; that is the meditation at night. Unless you come to that because you are drawn to it and wish for it; don't come. This is a privilege, to meditate. It is a gift that is graciously offered to us. To go to it reluctantly is to spurn, one may say, the gift that is offered. One should always look upon meditation in that way, and sometimes when one thinks, 'I don't want to go to meditation. I don't want to do this, I'm not in the right mood for it,' then one can say to oneself, 'But am I going to miss this chance that something may be given to me tonight, that I may have allowed it to slip?'

# Suffering

*We've been reading the Apocryphal Gospel of St. John in study sessions recently and there is a sentence that we could perhaps talk about – 'If thou hadst known how to suffer thou wouldst have been able not to suffer. Learn thou to suffer and thou shalt be able not to suffer.'*

In the Sermon on the Mount we are told 'Love your enemies, bless them that curse you, pray for them that despitefully use you and that persecute you.' This is ordinarily taken to be a requirement of humility, accepting injustice, of being compassionate and kind to people, and various virtues that are connected with this. But in reality it is, like everything in the Sermon on the Mount, a practical counsel for living. Without enemies we should have no chance.

Perhaps the most important creation was the Devil. How would the universe have had a chance of returning to the Source if there hadn't been a tempter in it? Ask yourself that. Why should one ever struggle and try to achieve anything, if there's nothing to struggle against? Therefore our enemies are necessary for us. We have to value them very much. And that includes our own inner enemies. If we had no egoism, then we should be like Angels, who are not capable of transformation. They can't be transformed because there is no denying principle. It is the same way with suffering. Without suffering there is no possibility of transformation. But the way in which suffering serves us is not just by giving us something to overcome, to be patient with, to be good about. The real thing about suffering is that it enables an action to proceed in the depths in us, it enables us to get below the surface, to get below even the ordinary depths, to find the place where there is no suffering. In everyone there is the place that is free from suffering. This place we have to find.

The way to it is through learning how to suffer and accept the action of suffering in ourselves; accepting it to the point where it is complete when the breakthrough comes, and we arrive at that place in us which is free. So it says 'If you knew how to suffer, then you would know how not to suffer'. Not-suffering does not mean being without any enemies or harmful actions. Not-suffering means to have entered into a particular place which is the sacred place inside us where there is no suffering, because it is a place of God. To find a way to that place is one of the great things. It is there that we come to the threshold of unity. So that saying is a good saying.

*I have been finding in the last few days that I've been very tired for no reason, not proportional to the amount of energy I've been using. When one is feeling like this, do you think that first it is better if you just really want to sleep, to go and do so, or to stop yourself doing it? And also, do you know from your experience why it is this happens, that, sometimes apart from personal reasons that one can trace, one's just very tired?*

This is where you have not got an assignable reason; you don't know if you've had too hard physical work or some emotional up-heaval?

*There are a few things I can trace. What I really want to know is how much one should just give in to this feeling and let it be.*

You understand that this is not a thing for which I can give you a general rule so it is always like this. There are two or three things I can say. First of all, especially if you are working in the kitchen, it may be, without your being aware of it, that it is affecting your breathing. You are not breathing properly. It may be more beneficial to you to go for a walk in the open air than to go to sleep. You may find that this fatigue will pass off by itself by giving your ordinary natural breathing a chance; because, you see, walking promotes natural breathing. This should be tried. I know myself that I some-times get very tired and I want to go to lie down for half an hour and I have to look at myself and say: 'Is it really rest that I need, or is it a change at this time?' But I can know myself well enough to be able to answer this and I can say: 'Well, I want to lie down, but really it's the right thing for me to go for half an hour's walk.' And I know that at the end of the half-hour's walk, the feeling of heavi-ness and tiredness and inability to make my body move will have gone. This is always worth finding out. Bound to our bodies, we have to learn that they are within the field of our knowledge. You know the saying 'You can know a horse, but you can't know a man.' In the same way you can know your body when you can't know yourself. This is one thing that Gurdjieff says. I was just reading from Talks with him last night. He was speaking about how in his teachings the first duty is to know one's body. First of all to know what it needs and to know when it is speaking the truth and when it isn't; when it's saying 'I am ill, I am tired,' is true and when it is not true. If you know horses well, then you can know anything, any animal body, well. But horses are particularly good for understanding people. You have to look upon your body in that same way: to know its tastes, its likes and dislikes, its needs, how much exercise is wanted, what food is required, how far you can take it, and when you have to stop driving it and so on. We take a lot of trouble to learn this about a horse but we take much less trouble to learn the same thing about our own body. That is one part of the answer.

I am not sure with you that there isn't something different from this. I think that it may be partly the psychic energy that is depleted and not only the physical. And the main means of replenishing one's psychic energy is through breathing.

*In terms of the previous question, I was wondering if you could say a little about the kinds of jobs we do and the way in which we do them. For example, if one does the same job that one likes very often, is it better to have a break and do something one doesn't like as much and doing it completely?*

In a monastery I go to, there was one very old monk who was in charge of the kitchen. The cooking there was a dream. Everything was so good. And he had a stroke and the Father Abbot put in another monk temporarily to do the cooking – that was I think about five years ago. This was more a task for him, because he didn't like the kitchen and perhaps had a tendency to think that he was a little too spiritual to be interested in food. Anyhow, he was put into the kitchen, and for rather a long time the food wasn't as good as it had been before. I went over there this year at Epiphany, and this monk was still cooking, having cooked for five years. And I thought with great interest that this had produced a great change in him, for the good. It must have been a very hard thing for him to do, but he did it out of obedience and he accepted to take this on. And in the middle of it all the Father Abbot, who put him in the kitchen, retired and went to Martinique. I think everyone thought that the new Abbot would let him off, but he didn't – the monk is still doing the cooking.

That is an exceptional case – to go right through for five years until something has actually gone; but there is in it a certain something which I am sure you can recognise, even if one cannot put it into words. At first he was doing the cooking out of obedience, then he was doing the cooking because he saw that it was a struggle with his own reluctance to do it; then he began to enjoy the cooking because he thought he had become a good cook; then finally at last, he lost interest in cooking, and just did cooking purely as a duty, with no feelings about it, and it left him free for his own meditation and con-templation. It no longer matters to him, I can really say that, whether he's cooking or not cooking. So probably he'll be taken off cooking.

Now this is one way of looking at it, to go through with something for a definite reason, for oneself. Even if it's not like that, I do believe that it's very good to be changing. For the last fifteen – twenty nearly – years, I have been watching the life of this monastery. It is of course very interesting to watch because the same people are there for ten, twenty, thirty years and they die there; and you can watch what happens to them in a perfectly stable environment and with a very wise teaching. I have seen it also in totally unstable conditions, or the kind of semi-stable conditions that we have at Sherborne. My own feeling is that it is important that people should not be doing a job just because they are good at it. If they go on doing a job, it should be because there is some definite benefit to them in doing it and it is better even that the community should suffer rather than that people should do a job just because they are the best person to do it.

*Mr Bennett, you've often said that it is necessary to suffer, and you've also talked about conscious suffering in the sense of actually putting yourself in the way of something. Is it necessary right from the start of one's path, or is it necessary at a particular stage that one does this, and is it done under direction? Could you speak a little about this?*

Certainly. Gurdjieff made a very sharp distinction between volun-tary suffering and intentional suffering. There is involuntary suffer-ing that we can't avoid – that can be used – but the suffering that comes because of our own actions is quite different in these two cases and this is not usually understood.

Voluntary suffering is suffering that one imposes on oneself for a definite aim, as an athlete diets himself, works himself, denies himself all sorts of pleasures. He makes his life exceedingly hard and puts himself in the control of a trainer – all because he wants to win or achieve something. That is the paradigm type of voluntary suffering. One can have voluntary suffering for the purpose of self-improvement. Let us take a simple case – I want to overcome unpunctuality or not getting up or something like that and I know that this has got to be cured, or I wish to cure it. And I say – well, whenever I'm late I will fast, deprive myself of food or do something or other, until I can make myself get up or not be late. All that is voluntary suffering because it is done for an aim that one has set oneself. In Gurdjieff's opinion this kind of suffering has relatively little value – the reward is the value of it. The athlete who obtains a high degree of proficiency has got that as his reward and he is admired and receives prizes. He himself doesn't get anything for his own being, for his perfecting, from it. Even when it is for the purpose of overcoming defects, this kind of voluntary suffering doesn't do more than overcome this defect and it may even misfire in this kind of way: the person, who with great efforts and in pain to himself overcomes laziness or unpunctuality, in the process also comes to think of himself as better than other people and thereby intolerant. The last state is worse than the first, as they say. So one has to look at voluntary suffering in these profit and loss terms. What am I trying to aim to achieve, is it worth going through all that to get to it? But intentional suffering is totally different.

Intentional suffering arises exclusively through actions for the good of others. The simple principle or paradigm of intentional suffering is, if one wishes to do good to somebody, to recognise that this is always going to mean more trouble than one reckons with, and so one must never do it for the sake of reward, but work for the welfare of one's neighbour by the conscious sacrifice of one's own. All that is really the basic, simple case of intentional suffering. It requires that one should understand the law. To do good is a privilege that one has to pay for, not something for which one will get a reward. If one wants to do something right, one will have to suffer for it – not merely that it is hard – it will bring some kind of painful consequences. A simple case is that it can bring ingratitude and can involve one in much more trouble than one reckoned with, that 'one thinks one has to go a mile and one finds that one has to go twain', as the

Sermon on the Mount puts it. Or you give a man your coat and he expects your cloak also.

We have all of us, at this moment, to work for the future. We have an obligation to serve the future, more than at most times in the history of the world. The world is entering a time of troubles and it will have to be served. Not just our own personal future but the future of the world. If we set ourselves to do this we shall incur trouble. We may pay for it beforehand, we may pay for it afterwards. We can't work for the future and expect life to be easy. That is the principle of intentional suffering. Whether or not you accept it, is another matter, but this is my own conviction that it is so. One can see it in the lives of great beings. The Buddha, after having gone through very hard times, and then finally given up all his austerities, all the voluntary suffering and hard living with his seven companions – which he'd partaken in for many years, thinking that he would achieve freedom from death and suffering by this austerity – finally saw that this was not giving him the result he wanted and so retired and went by the way of contemplation until he finally saw enlightenment. Then he wanted to share what he had received, at once he wanted to give – and immediately they all turned against him. They all thought that he was a renegade and rejected him. That is characteristic of what is called intentional suffering.

As soon as Muhammed had really received the revelation at Mount Hira, he at once lost his position. He had been the highly respected Muhammed El Amin, the reliable, the trustworthy Muhammed. Even his own family turned against him. He had to flee. He had to go across the Red Sea and take refuge. He had everything against him for years and years. The closest people, who he most cared about, had rejected him. One tends to think that the end of his life was a triumph. Yes, it was a triumph, but it lasted just three years, that's all. One hardly need say anything about Christ because his intentional suffering is the core of the Gospel story. So if we see that constantly being exemplified, then we should ask ourselves whether this is not a general law. That's what I believe. When one sets oneself out to serve mankind, know that this will bring one into trouble. Sometimes it is outward trouble and sometimes one has to suffer a great deal inwardly that nobody knows about.

There is, of course, the saying that no evil comes to the just man – also attributed to the Prophet – but this doesn't mean no suffering comes, it means that the just man is not deprived of his destiny. What happens to him is right for him. Take the story in the Gospel of the young man with the great possessions. He had done everything in the positive sense – he had fulfilled the law, he had been good and generous and so on. Then he was told – if you want to follow, then sell it all and give it to the poor. You may say that is voluntary suffering. No, it isn't, because – if you want to follow me, if you want to be perfect, then that is going to be the price, you must give everything away. This is not to get a specific result, not to achieve something – this is the main point where it is different from voluntary suffering.

*Is it possible that Abdul Qadir Gilani is an exception to this?*

Well, Hallaj was not an exception, let's say. Let's look at Abdul Qadir Gilani. How many children did he have? Thirty-two sons was it? I can't believe that they didn't cause him any suffering. They were all missionaries. The children and grandchildren of Gilani spread Islam in an extraordinary way. I don't know. I suppose I could put myself into Baghdad at that time and tell you something about the story. No, it is not that Abdul Qadir Gilani didn't suffer, it is that he was amazingly successful and that he wasn't rejected like the Prophet was rejected, but he had a very great burden to bear.

# Creative Imagination and Intention

*There is a question formulated in my mind, but I am not really sure why I want to ask this question; it has something to do with imagination. It tends to get played down as being something unreal which could distract us and I wondered whether you could say something about creative imagination in the spiritual sense.*

It is a very good question, a very important one and as so often happens with these things, I was talking about this very thing this morning. In the transformation of energies within us there are different stages. If you have ever read any of the Ouspensky or Gurdjieff books you will remember that he talks about the energy that comes from our food being transformed through different stages up to the action of air in the transformation. This is also to be found in Sufism – in fact it is a Sufi teaching. The sixth stage is when it comes to the sex energy. The one before that, the fifth (or what Gurdjieff calls *piandjoehary*), is the same as that which the alchemists call the quintessence, the fifth degree of refinement of the energy that we get from our food. This energy is the energy of imagination. It always is active – it is never possible to make this stand still – therefore either we use it positively or it uses itself. When it uses itself it produces in us daydreaming, fantasy, picture building, and so on. It is always there, and one of the great things we have to learn is how to control this energy. If we do continue to have these meetings I will come to this, but you cannot do it until you have learnt how to control the the fourth energy which comes before it.

The point about this is that it is two-edged. It can either waste our forces and turn us into dreamers, or it can, as you say, be creative. This has always been the teaching about this quintessence, that you must master it or it will master you. That is one way of putting it. It is the power by which creative work is done. It can be turned into thought forms or mental images that have power – this is why it is the essential element in magic. If you learn how to control this energy then you have power, but the first thing is to have power over yourself. When this begins to come to you it is a very strange thing because you realise that it is something completely different from self-control, since one has the power of command over oneself without having to struggle, and this comes from this particular energy. It can spontaneously produce creative images. It happens when one has tried very hard with some problem and the lower energies have become exhausted – then it is possible for this energy to come and you have the sudden solution of this problem coming into your mind without any apparent effort. It is very often when you have just given up trying.

When one talks about creative imagination you have to understand that people do use the word creativity in various ways; sometimes for the energy lower than this, which is inventiveness or ingenuity. When the fifth energy works particularly well in people, then they have what we call creative gifts, such as those of composers, artists and mathematicians. The real thing is to learn to use this positively, but then one has to be very careful only to use it in the right way. This is also a reason why in the schools that have this knowledge, people are not initiated into this until they have very good character – their character has been purified.

*Is the mastery over it something to do with the difference between subjective and objective art?*

Yes it is.

*Those things that you described seem to be more one's creative outward activity, but is there any sense in which it is used in oneself?*

Yes there is. In the decision exercises I showed to some of the people who are here, this energy is working. When you come to the fourth stage of the decision it is this energy that enables you to create the action you are going to carry out and then the connection is made with the higher centres. This is imagining in the right sense – one makes an image of the action one is going to carry out and in making that image we have to have the help of this energy. The centre of this energy is this chakra here (the forehead).

In some of the practices that are very common in Sufi *halkas* – for example, making a mental image of the *Sheikh* – this is working with the same thing. All this is not really in order to create the image of the *Sheikh*, but to get one to learn how to manage this energy. Later it does show it can bring one into a different world. In the Sufi schools, they come to the stage when they can see the founder of their order before them. If they are *Mevlevis*, they see Jalaluddin Rumi before them; or if they are *Naqshebandis*, then they see Bahaeddin Naqsheband in front of them. This is an indication for their own teacher that they have reached the stage where some important initiation is possible to them. The reason is that it proves that this energy is now working in them in such a way that it can connect them with a deep reality.

First of all you speak of the disparaging of imagination. This is entirely right because if one allows imagination to go without control it is simply wasting this very precious energy, and taking away the power of action. Thus one becomes a dreamer, 'building castles in Spain', and one does not face reality. That kind of thing comes from letting this energy work without any control, and it becomes a sort of self-indulgence; like sexual self indulgence, it is wasting a very precious energy. The other negative side of this is the wrong use of it – not wasting it, but using it in order to get power, which it can be used for, and people do do this. They may not know it, but if they have very great determination to achieve their own objectives and sacrifice everything to their ambitions, they do begin to use this energy and they begin to get power over people and that is one reason why all this is surrounded by precautions by people who know about it.

The energies of thought and feeling and sensation enter into our everyday life. They are the energies with which we know about the world, with which we form our opinions and attitudes. These energies are very habit forming and people do develop various habitual ways of thinking and feeling and so on, and because these energies have not got authority or power in themselves, they can very easily be instruments of egoism. Therefore one has to accept the importance of purification of the negative forces in us, at least to a point where they would not be dangerous if they gained power. For instance, if someone who is dominated by ill-will were to begin to get power of thought, that person can harm people if his ill-will is not just private, and his ill-will can easily project itself to damage people. One does not want to develop a higher power if there is a danger that it is going to be used in some wrong way like that. For it is not only that it can be harmful to others, as for example in a case of ill-will, it can be harmful to oneself. If one has no faith, if one does not believe that we are the servants of God, then we believe that if we have power we are entitled to use it. This can actually strengthen the coming of power because it can make us feel that we do not need God – that we can do it ourselves.

So, if one really wishes to become a perfected being, one must have a very strong wish to be pure, not to be a being with strength and able to exercise various occult or higher powers, with the possibility of exercising them in the wrong way from one's egoism. It is not enough to think that one should do it in a good way – one can easily deceive oneself. Many people who have acquired powers misuse them with the full belief that they are doing good. If someone – let us say like Adolf Hitler, who certainly acquired great power over people – becomes obsessed with this power, and then still continues to think he is doing good, and is able to exercise this power in a big way, then it becomes a very dangerous and terrible thing. I do not say that this often happens to that degree, but people can have powers and misuse them.

*A very important point is the commitment to either a positive or negative direction. . . .*

If it were so simple as that, it would be all right. But unfortunately, everyone thinks that they are choosing the good.

*It seems that in the use of the power of imagination one can affect everything, including one's dreams and one's experience of emotions and all sorts of things. Is it better to leave it alone altogether until you know how to use it positively to shape yourself?*

There are two things. First of all, it is much better to leave it alone. It is one thing to convince oneself that some thing is possible. Let's take the example of acid – LSD. This does release this energy. It can release the power of imagination – really extraordinary things – but it can also release power over oneself and this can be quite deluding because people will think 'I can fly, so I can jump off the top of a house', and sometimes they do. This is simply an easy way of seeing how dangerous it is to release this energy if one does not know what one is doing; also it can disturb the sex functioning because of that.

There are various ways without the use of acid or something equivalent to it by which one can release this energy artificially.

There are various kinds of tricks for doing it and anything like that is really dangerous. One should always be on the watch if one is interested or drawn towards any kind of school or teaching that promises things. You have to be on the watch whether they are offering these kind of powers. I know some that do. There is one in particular that has recently come into prominence that does this in a very simple but terribly dangerous way.

The other question is really about using this for one's own self-perfecting.

*. . . when one is always confronted with people who can learn from each other in a very simple way . . .*

Learn what from each other?

*Just to see one's imperfections through communicating with other people. Is it really necessary to know about all these things?*

It is necessary to *do*. What we can learn about our imperfections from other people is pretty limited, and if we do learn and wish to change we shall need a certain 'energy' at some time or other. We do not have to know the name of it, but it will have to come into it. Let us try to get to the bottom of what you are talking about. The question is: should we not be able, just by sharing our experience as it comes, to provide all that is necessary. It should be possible, and it would be possible if it were not that underneath this surface there are hidden away undesirable things in all of us, which we do not bring out and which are very difficult to talk about. You know I have a long experience in this. I know how hard it is when somebody very sincerely comes and asks me to talk to them about their problems, their defects, or whatever you were saying, for them to be able to see it. It is very hard to find a way first of all of seeing what the problem really is, then afterwards of speaking to them about it.

Gurdjieff, my teacher, was a man of extraordinary knowledge of human nature – really extraordinary. I have watched him with hundreds of people. When people came sincerely to him for help he would watch them. He would put them into various situations and perhaps it would be two, three, six months before he would give them any advice. Because even with such an insight as that, he needed to verify it – that he was really seeing what the problem was. I know myself how I was surprised that he spent such a long time before he told me what it was necessary for me to do. I thought he must see this at a glance. From my own experience I know how hard it is to help people unless they have got this inner eye at least to some extent woken up in them and they are able to see things for themselves.

Now, waking up this inner eye, this third eye – or as Gurdjieff calls it, higher emotional centre – I have spoken about it in various ways. Every teaching knows that there is some kind of inner perception in man that enables him to see things that he cannot see with his eyes or think about with his mind – that are beyond consciousness. My own experience is that people need to have help to awaken this in them, and then after that it is very different; then it is really possible to get to the bottom of their problems. This is where you have got to meet your own egoism. This is your real difficulty. If you cannot go as deep as that you can do things on the surface that seem to be putting things right, and then one day you have a terrible shock – you see that nothing really has changed. That shock comes to yourself sometimes when you think you have really made progress or really got somewhere, that you are really able to control yourself; and then you have this real shock of seeing that it was only on the surface and that it is still there just as it was all the time. So I am saying this to you, that helping one another would be fine if only it were not that many of our troubles are very deep. And I think everyone has got some difficulties quite deep down that they cannot reach just by thinking about it or by other people's observations. With one person it is a very deep-seated fear they have so hidden that they do not even know that they have got it. With another person it is a graspingness, the need to possess, that they can so cunningly hide from others and from themselves, that people do not realise that that person is like that because their behaviour may look quite different.

*How can you best tell whether or not you are fooling yourself about not having ill-will towards someone?*

I think you can, I think it is possible to ask oneself this kind of question. 'So and so, with whom I have had a bad experience – if I really look, can I say that I sincerely wish nothing but good to that person?' – And you really ask yourself. I feel that this is something that you can tell. You cannot do it in general, you cannot say in general 'Am I free from ill-will?' You look at particular situations and ask yourself – 'Do I fully accept this person, is there any rejection towards this person, can I really truly say that I love this person?' It certainly does require some practice because one can deceive oneself, almost pretend to oneself about this. I think that it is profitable to examine oneself in this way from time to time – not too much, because it becomes introspective.

*But when you ask this question and you know that there is an element somewhere that is rejecting. . . .*

That's good because then you are honest. . . .

*But do you still do whatever you were going to do because you should, or whatever it is, or do you not do it? I tend to do that all the time.*

Yes, that's right. If it is a question of getting rid of your ill-will, it is by action, by acting kindly towards a person. You said that it is not sincere, that I do not really feel what I am doing?

*Well it might be 95 per cent. . . .*

But supposing it was zero per cent – you might really want to see that person dead. You still can act as if you loved that person. This is one of the hardest things to understand, but just today's conversation perhaps makes its possible.

One kind of rule is that if you feel ill-will towards a person always act kindly, but if you know you are free from ill-will, sometimes you can act unkindly, you can criticise a person, when you are really sure that you love them. But coming to this point about this kind of insincerity, you have got to realise that the ill-will you might feel towards a person is really superficial. Deep down, really deep in yourself it is not there – if that person suddenly were to have a dreadful accident or misfortune, you would not in fact rejoice.

But let us suppose that there still remains something – deeper down is the place where all this would disappear. Ill-will can never penetrate deep down into one; it can start with one's egoism, but egoism is not the deepest thing in our nature, thank God there is something behind this. Therefore you can always say to yourself deep down this ill-will really is not there. I can imagine myself looking at this person from the real being inside me. This is where this power of imagination can really be very beneficial. One can say that I am going to look at this person as if I was Christ, as if I were a Saint. I imagine how would Christ look at this person. I can say, well, it is quite possible, it is not beyond our power to do that, because we have this imagination. That is what it enables us to do. When we begin to learn to use it then there are marvellous things that it can do for us.

It is quite true that we do keep out of the way – most people keep out of the way – of people we do not like or that produce some sort of uncomfortable reaction in us; and here I would say that the word 'should' can be used, one should get over this, one should not withdraw from people one feels uncomfortable with. One should learn how to be able to be all things with all men. And really it is part of one's own freedom. If I can only be at ease with some people and closed and withdrawn with other people it is slavery, it is weakness. I must be able to be friendly and open with everyone or if necessary withdraw from people who I may very much like to be with when there is some reason why I ought to withdraw. We need to have this power because we need to be free and sometimes you can look at it in that way. There is a person over there – there is no particular reason why I should go up and greet them in a friendly way, I know I could, or I could go on with my knitting or whatever it is. But you ask yourself 'Am I really free in this, am I not just running away? I may be avoiding something that will cost me just that amount of trouble.' After a time you begin to get a new kind of satisfaction and you begin to see how much better life is when you are able to be open with everyone whether you like it or not. I mean able to accept them, to feel good towards everyone. And not only feel good but act good. Is it enough to just sit in the corner and feel good?

# Baraqah
# St. George and the Dragon

*You were saying towards the end of your talk last week that it is now no longer possible for the normal teacher-pupil relationship to exist. This implies that the normal process of spiritual grace through a man is possibly no longer necessary.*

No; I didn't mean that this personal relationship of a teacher with one pupil is no longer possible, but no longer adequate. The world has grown, and its spiritual needs are so great that this restricted method of transmission is no longer sufficient. Certainly it continues, and will always continue. There is the universal *baraqah*. There is the *baraqah* of a particular tradition and there is personal *baraqah*. There are certain people who themselves acquire the power of blessing by their own merits. There are also people who, by playing a particular role in certain ritual conditions, are able to transmit blessing. In that case it is not one to one, but very often one to many, though both situations can come about. The third thing is universal *baraqah*, which pervades the world, and to which people become sensitive when their own inner enemy has been silenced. This inner enemy that we have in us stands at the door and prevents the entry of *baraqah*. Something stands at the door and intercepts what is destined for the real man (*insan*) within and can misuse it, and some protection against that is required. That is why everyone cannot draw by will on the universal *baraqah* and the spiritual power that is present everywhere.

So something is required, and this comes, as it were, through the ability to tune in; to resonate. If one is oneself out of harmony, if one is dominated by one's own *nafs al ammârah*, by one's own personal ego, then this is not possible. This universal *baraqah* acts in various different ways. But if, in anyone, this inner enemy is made peaceful and quiet, then the *baraqah* can reach. One thing we have to understand about our present time is that there is an intensification of this action, and therefore many people are touched by it. But it is a perilous thing because someone may be touched quite genuinely and receive this blessing and the power that goes with it, and then afterwards again be caught into his own egoism and misuse what he has received. Therefore there are various ways by which this is neutralised, so that no serious damage is done. But this is made so widely available because of the great need of the world at this time.

There are certain conditions which are favourable to receiving the universal *baraqah*. For example, when we stood together and turned our attention towards the Holy Prophet; this very pure being. What the Virgin Mary is for Christianity, Mohammed is for Islam; that is, the representation of the perfect, pure being, totally and wholly obedient to the Will of God. By turning our attention to this perfected, pure being, we can bring ourselves into a state which does allow this blessing power, or *baraqah*, to enter into us. But, if we are not deeply pacified, deeply peaceful, this is quickly disturbed again and its effect is transient. The real thing that is important for us is that we should be able to be sufficiently stable in our inner peace for this to be permanently with us and permanently acting in us. Therefore, some kind of preparation is needed.

In principle, when there is initiation, there is also probation, or preparation. It is necessary that those who have the power to initiate have the responsibility of seeing that they do not give what is holy to the dogs. The reason why I am glad to come down here and talk quite freely with you is that I do not feel any discordant notes. I feel able to talk.

*Is this universal* baraqah *more strongly in some places than in others?*

Yes.

*And how is that related to the particular energies of a place, or to the consciousness of the people in it?*

There are some places that have a right configuration, or right structure of their natural energies, and those places become sanctuaries. People feel them to be so, and then people come there and maybe a particular tradition remains in that place for a time and then goes, but another tradition will be drawn to the same place. I remember one place in Kurdistan – *Mar Behman*. It is very strange. As far back as anyone can tell, before Assyrian times, back to the Sumerian times, that particular place was regarded as sacred. It is very close to Nineveh. I cannot remember how close it is but it is a walking distance anyhow. When I was there – that is only about twenty-five years ago – it was a sacred spot for Christians, Muslims, Yezidis, and also for the Assyrian Christians. There were also Western Christian monks there, Franciscans. They all felt that this was a sacred place, and I felt it too. When we went down under the ground where the sanctuary was, you could not help feeling it, and it contrasted very strangely with Nineveh, which always produces a painful impression. This place was very holy. Mar Behman is the name of a Saint who lived about the third century. The strange thing is that when Hulagu, the grandson of Genghis Khan, was on his way down to conquer and destroy Baghdad, he stopped there and asked for a blessing for that place. The engraved stone is still there with Hulagu's command saying that nothing was ever to be requisitioned, and nobody was to be touched in that village. According to their tradition – but I've never been able to verify it – Hulagu ascribed his conquest of Arabia to the blessing he received from Mar Behman. All I know from my personal feeling in that place is that it was very extraordinarily sacred. I could name half a dozen places of that sort, that are now hardly known, nobody living very near.

*Is the universal* baraqah *particularised in nature, so that there is a* baraqah *from the animal kingdom and the plants?*

No, that is a different thing. That is not *baraqah*. The word *baraqah* is not used in that sense. It is a purely spiritual thing, and animals are natural. It does not mean that there is not a natural power that also is universal, but it is different. There is a life power that all life shares, every breathing creature shares in it, but this really is transmitted through the air. What I am talking about is beyond nature.

*We seem to be in a stage in world history when a lot of the closed cultural systems and their corresponding traditions that used to communicate* baraqah *are being opened up or destroyed. Is this connected with what you said, that we are at a stage where particular traditions for the teacher-pupil relationship are no longer feasible?*

I did not say they were no longer feasible. I said they were no longer adequate. Of course it exists, and everyone who can do so must find a teacher. It is very difficult to find a teacher, but because it is so difficult and because so very much has to be done, other methods are introduced. If the salvation of the world depended upon people who were initiated personally by teachers, there would not be a foundation on which to build. The necessary foundation would not be available if there were no other methods and other ways. The relationship of teacher to pupil is really a very high thing. People can enter into this relationship truly, only when they are very close to perfection. The teacher-pupil relationship is, and always has been, very exceptional. You read about teacher-pupil relationship; you read about Jalaluddin Rumi and Shamsi Tabriz, and things of this kind. These things give a picture of how it can be, but it is very rare. What I am saying is that there *is* this relationship, there *are* sources of real initiation, but people require very much preparation before they can come to them. The people who are capable of reaching that degree and whose task is to help the world must have many people through whom they can transmit, and the foundation has to be laid by this broader, and more broadly based, action. You've heard this saying that two hundred conscious men can save the world, or this notion in one Judaic tradition of the thirty-nine Just Men who keep the world from disaster. You must understand the implications of this. One Sufi tradition speaks of the forty *Abdal* and the *Qutb al zaman* or the *Mutasarrif al zaman*. But these are very exceptional. There are very few such people in the world. The world would be very lucky if at this moment there were really forty *Abdal*, who were capable of receiving directly from the Source, and who could have the great, the supreme teaching. But, if there is one man, who has reached a high degree of perfection, and he wishes to help others, he can do it in two ways. One is in secret by what he does inwardly inside himself. The other is by spreading outwardly, but in order to spread, he needs people who are already receptive. That is why I said there would not be enough foundation if there were not some universal action, and therefore it is happening at this time that literally millions of people are being touched. Especially among young people; more particularly among those who were born after the end of the last war, or after the year 1950, when the sins of the first half of this century had been expiated.

To be born after 1950 is really a very great advantage. I say that because it is from that time, from 1950, that it happened for some reason that a new development began. People disagree as to the year.

Some people say 1952 and so on, but many people who know what is
happening in the world, know that that was a crucial period, when
a great threat of disaster was averted. Since then, there has been a
very wide opening of this universal *baraqah*, and many people have
been touched by it; literally millions. Of those, some certain proportion are moved to search, and things begin to happen to them. They
begin to come into new contacts; they even begin to recognise that
there are people who look at the world in the same way, and who
cannot look at the world in the way in which they were taught to do
in their schools; by their society and by their elders and teachers,
and this begins to create in them a real hunger. This is not their own
doing. It is because this has acted on them and they have something
in them that is able to respond to it. That is the field of the harvest,
where the seed is sown. Various possibilities become known. People
begin to have specific kinds of hopes. But then they grow up, as in
the parable of the sower. The seed is sown and good seed grows up,
and so on. But, then comes the problem, which is expressed in the
words 'The harvest is plentiful, but the reapers are few'. The real
difficulty comes then, when there is a lack of means of tranmission
between the very great numbers, who could respond, and the very
few who are the custodians of the *baraqah*. The problem of the world
at this time is to bring these two together, closing that gap; how to
provide means by which people can be fitted to fill the gap. Those
who can, go a long way and come into contact with direct teaching
that is arranged from above. It is part of the working of the provi-
dential power that is at the present moment working in the world;
but what is left to us is really the filling of that gap.

    You know the picture of George and the Dragon. One traditional
treatment of the subject is that the lady, who represents the soul, is
there, and that St. George is there, and he is just looking at the
dragon, and the dragon, as long as his spear is just touching him, is
obedient, and the lady is able to lead him. The dragon, of course,
represents the *nafs al ammârah*. How can we master this dragon in
ourselves? The dragon is a necessary part of the drama. Eternal vigil-
ance is required; that is represented by St. George on his horse, with
his Spear, just touching the dragon's neck. That is all that is required.
As long as the dragon knows that he is watched, he is quiet and
peaceful. Then the soul, the *ruh*, represented by the woman, can lead
him on a silken thread. That is the state that we have to learn to
establish in ourselves. So long as the dragon was in the cave, he was

the threat. He could not be seen : what he would do next was un-predictable. When he was brought out of the cave and made visible; the whole of him visible to be seen, then this situation arose that St. George was able to control him. He was able to make him peaceful, make him quiet.

How does this allegory apply to our own spiritual life? The ordin-ary state of man is one in which he is identified with his dragon. His dragon is 'I'. The desires of his dragon are his desires. That is the state when the dragon is in the cave. There is no possibility even of fight-ing with him. The dragon is inside us and we are the dragon, that is the *nafs al ammârah*. This dragon will obey no one. It takes over; everything is done by it, it has taken command; it has usurped the position of the rightful ruler. How to see this; how to come to the point where one sees one's dragon as not oneself; how to arrive at having one's own St. George?

St. George did not come on this scene, you understand, a novice in the matter of dealing with dragons; he had probably been to a dragon-taming school. We have to learn little by little how to master what we can see in ourselves, how to master our destructive and negative impulses; our self-loving impulses. The dragon becomes weak in front of St. George. Then, a dreadful thing can happen : it can happen that St. George himself turns into a dragon. You must know that this is a dreadful risk that is run. If he ever thinks that he is the real beneficiary of the taming of the dragon, that the dragon has become his domestic animal, he will be in great danger. That is why the lady is there, representing the soul, the *ruh, ruhani*, the highest principle in man. Why is it feminine? Because it is obedient, it is loving; it is receptive, it is not seeking for power. She only holds the dragon with a silken thread. One can meditate on that picture. If you can see this in yourself, that your task in mastering your own negative part is not in order to gain command, but in order to be able to make this obedient, not to yourself, but to something other, that threefold situation is really the key to understanding about the *nafs al ammârah*. You have heard about the *nafs al ammârah*, and I see that you all know about it. Very good. If you could only really know about it!

*Mr. Bennett, could I ask you to explain what you meant when you said that there could be danger from the transformation of St. George into a dragon?*

It is not easy, if you've conquered a dragon, not to swagger a bit.

The real meaning of this is that one must have power as if not having it. There must be no satisfaction in having mastery of oneself. People attain mastery over themselves; they overcome fear, or anger, or some weakness in themselves, and then they ascribe this to their own merit. They begin to feel they are something, because they have overcome these things in themselves. That is how the danger arises, and it can be that this then becomes a worse dragon than the other.

*You spoke last week about ill-will, in relation to the purification of the heart. Could you say something about the other three things?*

The five obstacles or five hindrances, *vechas*, they are called in Buddhism.

You must understand that one must be on one's guard against collecting, against hoarding, as it were. I've told you about two; you think you will be better off if I tell you about five!

Ill-will and doubt. Ill-will is something one can cope with. It is possible for us to cope with it if we see that it shuts the door; that it is something from which it is necessary to be free. We must see that one must have goodwill towards all beings; hatred towards none, nor ill-will, nor any kind of inner rejection. The first thing is to see that it must be uncompromising. It is no use saying, 'I will bear no ill-will except to him, or her.' This freedom from ill-will must be impersonal, so that there is in one an automatic movement of goodwill towards every being. I had thought of suggesting that I should ask Bhante* to come down here, but he is leaving on Sunday. He has been leading us in the Buddhist meditation, and he always begins, as all Buddhist meditation always begins, by sending out goodwill towards all beings. This is right: one should do it. But, who is sending out goodwill? Is one oneself free from ill-will? How can I send goodwill towards all beings if somewhere in me there is some ill-will towards somebody? So it is necessary to be very watchful, to have a very great determination to rid oneself of ill-will, and little by little one will succeed. One must see by common sense that ill-will does nobody any good, least of all ourselves, and we must then open our hearts in this way, so that we have a very great wish to have a goodwill that is unshakeable towards all beings, especially beings like ourselves; human beings. And sometimes it is good to exercise oneself. If one had a movement of criticism or dislike towards someone, to see that this is put aside, to make sure that one has goodwill to-

* The Venerable (*visiting Sherborne House*).

wards that person. It is a matter of practice; of being aware of the necessity for us to be free from ill-will, and little by little this will come. It is the same with doubt. Doubt has to be distinguished from discrimination. Discrimination is necessary. Freedom from doubt does not mean freedom from discrimination, or the ability to recognise what is acceptable and what is not acceptable. Doubt is something else. It is based upon a wrong and egoistic demand, that one has the right to have evidence; that one has the right to have things proved to one. If one sees how doubt has its root in egoism, then one can see that putting away of doubt means putting away of a demand. We can see the way in front of us. For example, you who asked me if you really can overcome ill-will and doubt, or even diminish them: you remember, I did distinguish between getting rid of the dominance of these things and eradicating them totally. They belong to quite different stages of our self-perfecting. We can diminish these things very considerably but still have the traces, the possibility of movement. To come to the point where there is no possibility of any doubt or ill-will arising in one; that is already the state of a *wali*, already the state of a saint. To such a being a totally different destiny is already open. But I am talking simply about diminishing; how to have less of these things. To have less means that we must be prepared to give up a demand that things should be proved to us, for example, 'if this is true, prove it to me.' Jesus says, 'the wicked and adulterous generation seeketh after a sign, but there shall no sign be given them, save the sign of the Prophet Jonas.' If you understand that answer, you understand how one works against doubt. Were they entitled to ask for a sign? Was He not giving signs right and left? Why, on the other hand, was He giving signs everywhere, and then slapping people down because they came and asked Him for a sign? You have to see just what it is in you that asks for a sign, that says, 'prove it to me; give me evidence of this'. When you see this in yourself, you are actually able to let it go and accept what is in front of you. 'I can see the step in front of me, I don't need more; I have confidence that there is a benificent power in this universe, in this creation. I do not want to know what I am not ready to know. I do not ask for signs; proofs of anything.' – This is difficult. It is no easier to get rid of than ill-will, but one must see that though at first sight it does not look corresponding or similar, doubt is just as much the fruit of egoism as ill-will is. Doubt is really an illegitimate demand.

Always remember that by doubt I mean that which demands a sign, demands evidence. Not discrimination; that is quite different, it is a positive thing. When you look below the surface, you see that many things that people regard as quite reasonable and acceptable are so only because we all go on the premise that egoism is a legitimate part of man's nature.

*What is the translation of the words – 'nafs al ammârah'?*

*Nafs* means the spirit, or the soul, or the self. *Nafs* means oneself. I translated the words *nafs al ammârah*, myself, as the material self. *'Ammârah'* comes from the Arabic root meaning to command. It is literally 'the commanding self'. It is the dragon in possession. It is sometimes called the disobedient soul; the state of disobedience. The word *'nafs'* comes from the same root as *'nefes'*, the same of course as the Hebrew word *'nefech'* which means the soul or the spirit. There is the *nafs* and there is the *ruh*. The *ruh* and also *roh* – the same two words exist in Arabic and Hebrew alike – really means that which holds us to this world. When it is mastered, it is transformed; it is changed. It is still there, but it is serving a different master. In Sufi literature, there is such a bewildering variety of terminology that it is very hard to know all the terms, know their place, know how they connect with one another. There is what is called *nasut, jebberut, melekut* – you know that anyhow from *Ibn 'Arabi*. It is the *nafs al ammârah* that keeps us in the *nasut*.

*It seems that what you've been saying underlines the importance of both the belief in something outside oneself, and the correct understanding of how one can identify with it. Even in helping somebody else there's the danger of attributing* baraqah *to oneself.*

It is not we that speak, but 'the Spirit of God that speaketh in us'. One must never forget this. If I speak to you aware of the responsibility of fulfilling this role of interpreting teaching to you, then I am not speaking from myself, and I don't think what I am saying comes from me. But if we were to change the conversation and talk in some other way, and I were not filling this role, then I would be just as stupid and make just as many mistakes as anyone, and be just as feeble as anyone. One only gets this help when one is fulfilling a particular role. You get the help, because you are fulfilling the role of listeners. We are together in a certain ritual. This is a sacred thing, when the *Sohbat* occurs. You know *sohbat*? It is a technical term in Sufism for the kind of event that is happening now, that is, where there is a talk about spiritual matters and someone is taking on the role of being the interpreter to others. Everyone is contributing to the creation of this kind of situation so that we are able to talk together in this way. What you are saying is very important. One must always be careful not to ascribe anything to oneself. If the thought can arise in one's mind that, 'I am saying this. I know,' then one must again put the spear into the neck of that dragon.

# Khidr - The Four Worlds - Needs

What I would say about Khidr would depend upon whom I was talking with. One way to speak about it is that there are powers that act from the spiritual world in this world and take forms, which are not always visible. Sometimes these powers take the forms of myths or they assume some image. Closely connected with Khidr is the notion of Elijah, a special prophet who is venerated by people of all religions in the Near and Middle East. It does not matter whether you are a Muslim, Jew, Christian, Yezidi, there is the notion of Elijah, and of the prophet who is able to come in any form from Heaven.

The kind of things one can say about Elijah one can say about Khidr. But you have to understand that this is presented to people to provoke in them an image of something that in fact cannot be imagined and cannot be described. So this kind of image is created; but it is created from above, it is not created by man. That is why I say it would depend whom I was talking to. Do I talk to people who need images or people who do not need images?

*Why is Khidr associated with the colour green?*

That is why I connect it with Elijah. There is in this a notion of resurrection, of ascending to Heaven, connected with renewal and therefore with greenness. It is another thing if you really understand that green comes out of nowhere – there is not really such a thing as green light. What we see as green in the rainbow is simply due to overlapping. Sometimes the rainbow divides in such a way that you see there is no green in it. Green is only seen as reflected light, in leaves and so on. So that although it is the real colour of this earth and green represents so much to us – yet there is no green light. This is very strange, because the power of Khidr is only in manifestation – it is not an independent being. However, I find the things that I should say to you about Khidr would have to be translated and adapted. I cannot talk directly about it. I have this feeling when you speak about Khidr – I am saying to myself 'But Khidr doesn't belong to this world and why is it that we are talking about him? Because for this world he is only a myth or an image.' Therefore when you talk about Khidr, you have to talk about the particular world where Khidr is much more real than we are – *Melekut*. But here in this world we are real and Khidr is only a myth.

*What is meant by the next world?*

Melekut is really the next but one. Khidr is beyond the next world.

*Can you say something about the next two worlds?*

You see one of the difficulties about Sufism is the proliferation of terminologies. Each different school has a different way of talking about the same thing. I can't go back in my own mind and say that 'this is how Ibn 'Arabi talks about it' – yet you are following his line. I am saying all this because I don't want to be confusing if I talk about technical things. So I think if you want me to talk about this I had better not use the Arabic words, in case they should not be the same words. Words like *Melekut* and *Jebberut* you are accustomed to, of course, and *Nasut*.

*Nasut*, really means the human world – this world of our human affairs. It isn't really a world – it is a way of perceiving – it is our human environment where we live in this state of separation from one another, each enclosed in our own life, and not aware of how we are connected with one another. The other way of speaking about it, and this is the way I want to talk about it here, is to talk about it in terms of what kind of existence that is. I can talk about that to you.

Is there anything else that anyone would like me to talk about, because this will take up the rest of the time? You see what I want is that my visits here should be useful to you and I must leave it to you to say what you think is useful. If you think it is useful for me to speak about the worlds, then I will.

*(Someone asks again about Khidr)*

Well, I had better ask you what Khidr means to you. There are many popular stories about Khidr and Moses etc., but this is just mythology. You mean how can you get beyond the image of Khidr to for example, the objective vision which is attributed to Khidr. This is in the Koran, of course, and is not just literature.

'So they found one of Our servants, on whom We had bestowed mercy from Ourselves and whom We had taught knowledge from

Our own Presence. Moses said to him : "May I follow thee, on the footing that thou teach me something of the (Higher) Truth which thou hast been taught ?"

'Khidr (The other) said : "Verily thou wilt not be able to have patience with me. And how canst thou have patience about things about which thy understanding is not complete ?"

'Moses said : "Thou wilt find me, if Allah so will, (Truly) patient : nor shall I disobey thee in aught."

'The other said : "If then thou wouldst follow me, ask me no questions about anything until I myself speak to thee concerning it."

'So they both proceeded until, when they were in the boat, he scuttled it. Said Moses : "Hast thou scuttled it in order to drown those in it ? Truly a strange thing hast thou done !"

'He answered : "Did I not tell thee that thou canst have no patience with me ?"

'Moses said : "Rebuke me not for forgetting, nor grieve me by raising difficulties in my case."

'Then they proceeded : until, when they met a young man, he slew him. Moses said : "Hast thou slain an innocent person who had slain none ? Truly a foul (unheard-of) thing hast thou done !"

'He answered : "Did I not tell thee that thou canst have no patience with me ?"

'(Moses) said : "If ever I ask thee about anything after this, keep me not in thy company : then wouldst thou have received (full) excuse from my side."

'Then they proceeded : Until, when they came to the inhabitants of a town, they asked for food, but they refused them hospitality. They found there a wall on the point of falling down, but he set it up straight. (Moses) said : "If thou hadst wished, surely thou couldst have exacted some recompense for it !"

'He answered : "This is the parting between me and thee : now will I tell thee the interpretation of (those things) over which thou wast unable to hold patience. As for the boat, it belonged to certain men in dire want : they plied on the water : I but wished to render it unserviceable, for there was after them a certain king who seized on every boat by force. As for the youth, his parents were people of Faith, and we feared that he would grieve them by obstinate rebellion and ingratitude (to Allah and man). So we desired that their Lord  would give them in exchange (a son) better in purity (of conduct) and closer in affection. As for the wall, it belonged to two youths, orphans, in the Town; there was, beneath it, a buried treasure, to which they were entitled; their father had been a righteous man : so thy Lord desired that they should attain their age of full strength and get out their treasure – a mercy (and favour) from thy Lord. I did it not of my own accord. Such is the interpretation of (those things) over which thou wast unable to hold patience." ' – Koran; Sura XVIII, 65-82.

You understand this story is clearly told here in the Koran as a teaching. It is a vehicle for expressing something and is not to be taken as a historical story. That is why I say that in this world Khidr is only a myth or a fable. But that does not mean that there is not a reality : there is a source, there is a means of transmission, a way through which revelation flows that is not through visible prophets. You see the difficulty is that I can only talk about such things that are written. Of course very many Sufi writers have taken up this story and presented it in all their varying ways and that is what it was intended for. But at the same time it would not be in the Koran if it were only that, because the Koran is a sacred book and there is something more behind it.

Therefore, we can be sure that there is a source of wisdom from beyond this world that is of the same nature as the prophetic revelations; but is not manifested and is only revealed indirectly. It is all that which is conveyed by Khidr. If you study it carefully, you will see also that it means that there is a hidden meaning. The great question in Islam is whether there is a secret teaching; whether or not there is an esoteric doctrine in Islam. All the Sufis and mystics say there is and that it was transmitted through Ali, whereas the exoteric or 'shari'ah' was transmitted through Abu Bakr. They say that we have two lines, one coming from Abu Bakr, and one from Ali; and most Sufis trace their 'way' back to Ali, though in some cases to Abu Bakr. But the point is that with the orthodox tradition which is based entirely on the Koran, there are included the kind of passages that make it orthodox and permissible to assume that there is also a secret teaching which is revealed only under special circumstances. That is really the importance about Khidr. If there were not passages of this kind in the Koran, people who say that there is no secret teaching would be able to quote the Koran in support of it. Whereas those who say there is a secret teaching are able to refer to something. I think that there is and was a secret teaching. But to go further would be to talk about the teaching itself and that I am not here to do; so maybe we can go back to this teaching about the worlds.

All religions must believe that there are other worlds than this. In the Christian tradition there is the belief in this present world and in some intermediate state that the soul enters into after death if it is not pure enough to go to the world which is directly in the Light of God, in the Beatific Vision. These worlds all have different gradations, as is taught explicitly by *Dionysius*, and this forms part of the Christian Orthodox tradition. It is said that there are not only other worlds, but different states in other worlds, chiefly because of the specific reference of Jesus, which is similar to a passage in the Koran (the Cave), 'In my Father's house there are many mansions'. In other words there are different states which it is possible to enter according to the degree of purity. The same, of course, is taught in Islam; and the same in Hinduism and Buddhism. The teaching is particularly clear and good in the Hindu tradition, in making the distinction between form and formless worlds : *'Rupa Loka'* and the *'Arupa Loka'*. This is very important – if you can really get some idea of this, then many things about the higher worlds can be grasped. According to the Sufi tradition there are two worlds of form and two formless worlds. This is more or less what is taught also in Buddhism and in Hinduism and in a less clear way in Christianity too. It would be quite easy to cite passages from the New Testament which would fit in with the idea of these four worlds.

The first world is the 'World of Bodies'. In Arabic it is the *'Alemi edjsam'* (*edjsam* comes from *jesm, jesm* means any bodily thing). This is the world of our sense perceptions, of our lives here on earth. It is the state of incarnation, living in this physical world. We entered it at conception and we leave it at death. This is the first world.

The second world is called the *'Alemi Erwah'*. *'Erwah'* is the plural of *'ruh'* which means spirit. It is the world of spirits. This world also has forms, but the forms are different – they haven't got the same constraints or limitations of the bodily forms that we know. In this world there are all kinds of spiritual existences – they also have form, but the form can change. There are many gradations in this world; the first is where it is in contact with the visible world, the world of tangible bodies. The most primitive state of existence in this world is the state of dreaming, where one is out of touch with the world of bodies but still living as if one were in the world of bodies. One still perceives forms and the forms are all the same as of the bodily world. That is the first level. There are spirit forms that are freer than that and which are on higher levels. This is one of the things in the Koran that you are required to believe if you are a true Muslim, – angels and spirits, and of course the *Jinn*, referred to in the Koran as beings who live in this world. There is a certain tendency to turn this into something figurative, but there is no doubt that this was not only taken literally by the early Muslims and by Muslims up to our time, but it played a real part. It was required that one should believe in the angels – I do not know if you were required to believe in the *Jinns*. You are certainly required to believe in *Iblis* who is a *Jinn*. You see this also in the Christian tradition, in the Celestial Hierarchy and even in the preface to the mass where 'angels and archangels and all the company of Heaven' are spoken of. So somehow or other this is accepted, at least verbally, if not mentally, at the present time. In Buddhism how it is treated is extremely interesting. In the very oldest scriptures – which are probably nearest to the language of the Buddha – the *'Pali Pitikas'*, there are several occasions when Buddha is asked the question – 'But are there gods, are there spiritual beings?' and he answers that of course there are, this I knew off hand, but there is nothing to this. If your perceptions are fine enough, you can see and perceive them, but what does it matter to you?

The other day we had with us a Buddhist monk who was talking about his experience in the forest, of having seen spirit beings, and how frightened the villagers were of them. I think there is a mistake we make in our wish to try and get away from superstition – which is quite a legitimate and right wish – because in throwing away superstition, we also turn our back on the reality behind it, the kind of relationships we can have with the spirit beings that form the subject of superstition. When I was talking about this the other day, I said that in this *'Alemi edjsam'* there are enormous differences of being. A stone, a plant, an animal and a man are all enormously different and man is by no means the highest that will be attained on this planet in the form of incarnate existence. If we can see how great these differences are, perhaps we can picture to ourselves that there are equally great, perhaps even greater differences, in the spirit world – the *'Alemi Erwah'*.

This is the world that you primarily enter after the death of the physical body. We do enter this world in dreams, but on a very primitive level; unless they are exceptional dreams which have a message or a teaching in them, which come from a higher level, though from that same world. There is very much that can be learnt and understood, and needs to be said, about the '*Alemi Erwah*'. We have disregarded it too much and we disregard the possibility of our co-operating with this world; not only in being helped by it, but also helping with it in its work; because there are high spiritual beings that have, especially in this time in history, heavy, almost impossible tasks in helping mankind through this present stage of transition, which wouldn't be possible without this help. All that (and obviously one could go on a long time talking about this world) you find many references to it in Muslim literature – in all literature. People can have direct experience of this world – I certainly have – I have no doubt about it. But it is still a world of form. It still has its limitations. It is not limited in space and time in the way that the body world is limited, but it has its own limitations. It has one more dimension than this world, and very strange and important things happen here that I could talk about and which are very interesting. For example, we can meet one another in this world and I could talk about what can happen in this kind of meeting. But that is enough.

Now we come to talking about the worlds without form that can be called non-material or in the true sense 'spiritual'. You can talk about a spirit world or a world of powers that do not need form. This world, in the terminology that I am following now, is called the '*Alemi Imkan*'. This comes from the same root as '*mumkin*', the possible. It is the world of potentialities, the world out of which the creative power enters into the worlds of form. This is the same, for example, as *Jebberut*. In this world the Will of God acts directly. It is said that in the form-worlds the Will of God acts through the laws and through spiritual powers, through angels and through beings, and through us, but not directly. In the third world, the world of potential and power – *Jebberut* – God's Will is present. This is where Khidr really is.

It is not even possible to speak about Absolute Being, but that is why the word '*Hu*' when it is used in that way does not stand for a being. It stands for that Source from which Being comes. It is the same as that which in Buddhism is called *Nirvana*. *Nirvana* means that state which is beyond Being. Therefore looked at from the side of Being it appears to be empty nothingness – just as from our side silence simply appears as the absence of sound, but silence in itself is far more than sound. Silence only appears empty when you are looking for sound, and if you don't find sound, you say that there is no sound here. But if you enter into silence, you become aware that sound is an intrusion. You realise how much greater silence is than sound. The same way that you realise that the emptiness that has no attributes is very much greater than any attribute. These things one can have some kind of acceptance of, and it is at this point that all religions, all teachings, unite. This is the transcendental source of all religions.

In the world of forms religions differ from one another. In the world of bodies, they can conflict with one another and one teaching can exclude another teaching and everything can be seen only relatively. In the second world, in the world of spirits, religions have the same form, because the forms no longer have that fixedness. This means, for example, that two saints who meet in the world of spirits would not have any questions such as 'Are you a Christian, are you a Muslim, are you a Jew?' and so on. They would recognise one another and would not be concerned with form. In the third world certainly all religions are one, but in another sense. They are all manifestations of the power of God. But in the fourth world they are all one in another sense, that they are all lost in the same source. Their differences are not merely from the same manifestation of God, but they disappear altogether.

I realise that the reason why I keep thinking that I am speaking about it again is that I have spoken about it so often recently at Sherborne, because we have been doing meditation on the four worlds. But I hope that I have not said anything that conflicts with what you read in Ibn 'Arabi.

It is so Universal and so ancient that it is very difficult to say that the Christians borrowed from the Greeks or that the Greeks borrowed from the Zoroastrians or that the Jews borrowed from the Magi. However, this notion is widely accepted and to me it is really clear. Our difficulty is how to be sufficiently detached. It is really a very great detachment that enables one to become aware of how there are things beyond form – reality beyond form. The third world can also be called the world of will.

*What is a need?*

There are real needs and there are imaginary needs. Real needs are very powerful things. There is the need of a child who can provide nothing for itself. This helplessness of the child is one of the most powerful things in the world. How great a part of human endeavour goes into providing for the needs of children! As long as they can't provide for themselves their need is able to make people work for them and obey them in quite a different way from any obedience to authority. It is impossible for anyone who is not quite insensitive to hear a child crying and not feel the need to do something about it – feel concerned, feel compelled to give his attention. This I am saying to show that need is a very powerful thing in the world and our own need is put into us because without need we wouldn't do anything. So we also have our own need.

Now the question is, how far do we need other people's support? The answer is that in so far as we are children we need it. It is no good thinking that we can act as if we were independent if we have not yet reached that stage of independence. The truly free person doesn't need the support of others, any more than the child when he is grown up. He is able to earn food and produce it for himself. If we let these needs go on and don't grow up, then this means that we lose our possibilities. You must realise that needing the attention and sympathy and friendly attitudes of people towards you is a childish thing. It is a psychic childishness that only up to a point is required. A human child requires this and it is an obligation for us. We have to give it. It is not enough to supply their bodily needs, we have also to give them a feeling of assurance in this strange world into which they have been brought – for children have come out of the higher worlds into this world of separateness and they need something to compensate. But if we're on our way back to the other world, then we have to learn how to become independent of this.

You were asking the question whether this dependence on others, upon the feelings and attitudes and behaviour of other people, is given to us as a means for our liberation. Your question is a very good one. You see there is a deep sense in which we need one another – not simply relatively, but absolutely. That need is over-riding. The thing is, there is a false need which tends to hold us to this world: this is a need for something outside. You see, if we were both in another world then we can meet one another from the inside. This belongs to the second world.

There is a real objective need for one another, and this separateness that is the result of our living in bodies is a limitation that we want to overcome. But there is a peculiar false need, and that I think you have quite well recognised, which gets in the way of our finding the deeper one. If I am minding about what people are thinking about me and what they say about me, I am treating the whole thing on a superficial level. It is not touching either the real part of myself or the real part of the other person. And therefore this kind of thing, and all the kind of sentimental attitudes that have an affinity with it, are an obstacle to our reaching the other : the real need we have objectively of one another, and the real acceptance of one another and real love for one another. The other need which you were talking about, as you can see for yourself, always involves something egoistic, it has got a demand in it. With all that we are really pushing other people away. If we can get rid of all that and understand it is possible for us to be one, then it becomes very silly that we mind what we say to one another.

*It seems that in the search for independence it is so imperative to know oneself. This understanding of the two different needs can only come through that certainty.*

Yes it is so. If you can really see where it comes from, then you are already half free from it. You see, in the ordinary way people don't ask this sort of question because they make demands. Even if they don't do it outwardly, inwardly they are demanding that they should be appreciated, that they should be understood, accepted and so on. But in doing that they are really rejecting the other person because they are saying to the other person, in effect : 'You be just the kind of person that I want you to be – not yourself, but the kind of person who is going to behave just as I want you to behave.' So this apparent care and feeling for other people is really a rejection of other people. When you can accept people whether they are pleasant, or unpleasant, or whether they flatter you or whether they distress you, whether they take from you or whether they give to you, then you are not rejecting them, then they can enter into you, then the real need can come out.

# Beyond the Veil of Consciousness

Everyone who is a Sufi or aspires to be a Sufi knows that our consciousness is a veil that hides reality from us (*haqq, haqiqah*). All of us hope that this veil will be lifted, so that we can see what is beyond it. Can one talk about what is beyond the veil of consciousness? I would like you to ask yourself about this phrase, which you have no doubt heard many times, whether you have brought yourself to the point where this veil is in front of you and you feel that there is something behind it.

In, I think, the Reshahat Naqshebandi of Mohammed Bahaeddin Naqshebandi of Bokhara, he describes an experience he had. If you don't know it, I'll tell you this story. You know he was one of the great Sufis of the fifteenth century and commonly called the founder of the Naqshebandi Order, but the truth is that these people who were called founders, never were founders. They were just great beings, with great illumination, who were able to transmit something to their own *khalifahs*, but it was usually the second *khalifah* who in fact set up something which continued in some kind of organised form. So when one talks of Bahaeddin as the founder of the Naqshebandi Order, it is a mistake, just as it would be a mistake to call Jalaluddin Rumi the founder of the Mevlevis, because I think the last thing he had in his mind was to found anything or to set up any organisation. Nor did Husam al-Din, but it came up with his second *khalifah* also. So coming back to this story of Bahaeddin: he did have extraordinary experiences when he was a young man, and he used to like to go to the graveyard to pray and to meditate. One night he went out asking himself, 'What tomb shall I go to pray at tonight,' And then it came to him to go to the tomb of such and such (I can't remember which of the great Sufis it was) of Bokhara. So he went there, and then he saw a light on another tomb and went to that tomb. Then a horseman came along and he joined him and went with him on the horse. Then he found himself, in a vision, in a great place with many of the great Sufi masters around him. But before him was a veil, and he knew that behind the veil there was somebody sitting on a throne. Bahaeddin had been given the headpiece of another great Sufi when he was quite a young boy and he saw this over in one corner. Then somebody said to him – 'It is because you have that headpiece, and it is because that has been given to you, that you are here'. Then they said to him, 'You can go and lift this veil yourself', and he saw Abdülhalik Gücdüvânî sitting on the throne, who then initiated him. But of course the meaning of this is that it is given to very few to lift the veil themselves, that hides the reality beyond. For most people this lifting of the veil is beyond their own power. When he was old, Bahaeddin once said, 'When I was a young man, I prayed to God that he would give me every kind of hardship and make me go through every kind of trial that is possible for people to go through.' This was given to him and, having accomplished it, he saw that this was no longer necessary. He had that kind of determination. He was that kind of man, a very rare kind, who not only does not avoid any difficulties, but actually puts himself in the way of the utmost difficulty and the utmost hardship in order to attain this aim of liberation. For such people, the lifting of the veil is something that is given to them to do. In another of his visions he found the Prophet in front of him, and the Prophet said, 'Carry me to the top of that mountain.' And he took Mohammed on his back and carried him to the top of a mountain, which is quite an achievement. And when he got to the top of the mountain, the Prophet said to him, 'Of course I knew you could carry me, but I wanted you to realise for yourself that you could do it.'

So, I want to talk about how we can understand this 'Beyond the veil of consciousness.' Very few can realise that behind it there is another concourse. When the veil was lifted, Bahaeddin saw a number of masters of ancient times who were all present together, and of course he saw other realities and many things were revealed to him which he did not, and could not write about. This can also be put in a figurative way; this greatness beyond the veil. But these are all things that we can use words for. We have to accept that what is beyond the veil is of such a nature that no words can be used. When I was sitting in front of you here and asking myself, 'What am I going to speak about?' the answer came, 'You can speak about what is beyond the veil of consciousness.' I thought, the only way to do that is to say nothing, because about what is beyond the veil of consciousness nothing can be said. But questions can be asked. This is the peculiar nature of questions, that they don't have the same limiting character as answers and statements. If one can avoid saying anything, if one can ask a question and not expect an answer, if one can look at a mystery and not expect it to be revealed, if we can look at the veil of consciousness and not expect it to be lifted – this is why from time immemorial the asking of questions has been regarded as a more penetrating thing than the giving of answers. The asking of questions is really within the power of all of us. This is why I ask this question, and we can all ask ourselves, 'What is beyond the veil of consciousness? What is hidden from us by the nature of our own consciousness?'

Some explanations can be given about this. Two very different things can be said. One can speak about the expansion of consciousness, the deepening and broadening of consciousness, and one can speak about going beyond consciousness. One should really understand with one's whole mind that these are totally different things. One thinks consciousness can expand until one is able to embrace the whole universe, and still remain on this side of the veil. One can have cosmic consciousness – such an expansion, such an ecstasy, that everything is revealed. But it is still this world that is being revealed to us, with its greatness, its marvels and so on; its time, past and future. Even if it is in incomprehensible images which are not yet appreciated by man's thinking, or which have been forgotten by man's thinking, even if the images are quite incomprehensible and cannot be explained in ordinary terms, these images are still consciousness.

We turn from this Sufi account to the Hindu account of it. When the Hindus speak about it, they do speak about this state, this *Sushupti* state, as 'being taken out of consciousness' – not, as it is sometimes translated to be 'dreamless sleep' – a very meaningless phrase, because dreams or not-dreams is beside the point. But what is it that happens to someone whose consciousness is interrupted, who is in a state of real rapture, where there is no consciousness? All he knows about it is that when he returns to his ordinary state of consciousness, he remembers that he has seen what he never could see, and he can hardly remember even the glimpse that comes to him at the moment of transition between the two worlds. What happens to him when he is really in the other world he cannot remember at all. So, when does it happen that there can be a bridging of the gap between the two, and in what way is this gap impenetrable? It is impenetrable largely because of our own ignorance.

Again we change, from looking at it in terms of Hindu to Buddhist. For the Buddhist (I am talking now of the Terevadin Buddhists of the Nikayas) the final stage before the awakening, the Enlightenment, comes when there is delivery from the desire for existence, from ignorance, from any kind of self-willed action. These three final obstacles, the desire to act, the desire to be, and the belief that one knows or understands anything. When one is free from these things, then, they say, comes the liberation, then they become the *Bhodi-sattva*, the fully enlightened.

Every religion, every teaching is concerned with this transition from the imprisonment within this world and the liberation into the other world. But very often, what is said, especially by people who write about this, shows that they have a confusion of ideas about consciousness. They think that to be more conscious, to have a wider, greater expanse, a more all-embracing consciousness, is to progress in the right direction; that to understand, to experience more, to be able to embrace more, have visions of the past, to be able to enter into one's past lives, to be able to see the future, to be able to understand the laws of the world : all of this kind of thing can come with an expansion and transformation of consciousness. But this can all be simply enlarging the prison. The other direction, the direction into nothingness, into the disappearance of the self, this is the direction that is beyond consciousness.

Everyone hears these words, like annihilation, cessation of existence, ceasing to be. But what is the *Maha para Nipana*, (a phrase from the Buddhist terminology), the great ultimate liberation, the great ultimate annihilation ? Then all the stupid questions are asked; 'And afterwards, after this ultimate, final liberation, does the Buddha exist, or doesn't he exist ? Is he there or is he not there, or is he both there and not there ?' And the answer is no, no; this is none of these things. He is not there, he is not not there, he is not both there and not there. I try to make you ask the unanswerable question. In the way of the Zen masters, this asking of unanswerable questions becomes just a practical technique for preparing one for the step of surrendering one's illusion of self. You may say, 'Well, if the Buddha would not answer the question, "What is beyond consciousness?" and if nobody will answer this question for us, what is the use of our asking it?' This is not right. It is by holding oneself in front of this extraordinary thing that one can learn. We human beings are so made that we have one side of our nature belonging to that world which is beyond consciousness, and this is the special, very peculiar thing about man. We naturally pride ourselves on the possession of these extraordinary instruments, this beautiful body of ours, with such a high capacity for adaptation exceeding that of any other animal, not the individual powers of animals in every case, which can be higher than ours, but our power of adaptation. Not the extra-ordinary range of feeling experiences which man can have, which perhaps in totality, the animals, all beasts and birds together perhaps have the same range of feeling experiences that are possible for man. But man alone has the whole thing, although of course he forfeits his birthright by allowing himself to live with selfish, petty emotions, but he does have the possibility of a real emotional life. He has this instrument, this thought of his power to project himself, not only into the past and in the future but even out of space and time. And yet with all of that, we are only talking when we say all those things, and we have said everything that we can say about man's knowable nature. All that can enter into his consciousness. We have not begun to penetrate into the mystery of man, have not *begun* to penetrate.

When Hallaj said *'Ana'l Haqq'* – 'What is this'; we say – 'Blasphemy, or rapture or ecstasy or something?' But the real truth is that when the veil is broken, then things are so different that one dares to say man becomes infinite and God becomes small. Here we sit in front of this veil; for the most part people turn their backs, look out, look away from it, look away towards the more limited, the more restricted world, the world of these material transformations. They look at the outward manifestations of people, and all of this is turning one's back. Of course we have to do this; it is our obligation, it is required that we should do this. But, one can feel that when one is doing this, one is temporarily, for a time, because one is obliged to, looking at this outer world, knowing that one's reality is in the other way. Can we really feel that this world only exists because we are obliged to do something about it, that it doesn't exist in its own right and that if we identify ourselves with it, we also cease to signify anything? Can we see this world really as a world where man has only a mission to fulfil, no place, where truly nothing can touch him? He is only there because he has something to do there, not because he belongs to it? When we turn in the other direction and look at this – 'If this is lifted for me, what will happen to me? Will I be consumed? Will I disappear?' Perhaps the moment comes when one gets near to this, and even a certain real terror comes over one. What would it mean to go through there? For the most part people do not have this terror because they do not come close enough to see the abyss.

We speak about finding ourselves in front of a veil. I want to go back to what I quoted from the Bahaeddin story, that behind the veil there was someone there, there was not a blank, not nothingness at all, not images, but actual people. That is the thing that we must hold on to if we can. Although we are aware that when we turn towards the depths, we are in front of something that we cannot penetrate with our ordinary consciousness, it does not mean that what is on the other side is blank, just because our consciousness can't seize it. There is a very strange thing in the Mathnawi of Jalaluddin Rumi. He says: 'You want to find the work; seek the worker. The worker is in the workshop. The workshop is the workshop of nonentity. The workshop is in the place of non-existence.' Then the whole thing goes on, embroidering on this. But he emphasises that this is the place of doing, the place of work, of activity, and at the same time it is non-existence. This one can say to oneself: 'When I'm in front of this am I feeling that I'm not in front of an emptiness but that I'm in front of something which is different and perhaps to my ordinary consciousness would appear empty?' As it is rightly shown in the picture from the 'Republic' of Plato – that one doesn't see because the light is too bright. But it doesn't mean that in the light there is nothing but light. The free earth is there for those who can return into the light. The light enables them to see what they have to do and what is really to be done. Certainly that picture of Plato's is full of meaning. It can be read in a very simple way but there is more to it if one looks at it differently. I would say that one can, by contemplating this, come to the conclusion that it is not possible that our lives should be confined to this consciousness, in which we are aware that there must be another part of our nature, and that this nature we must share with many other things. There is, in other words, another world, and we are prevented from communicating with this world because we are communicating from the wrong place in us, that is, from our minds and our feelings, all of which are limited by our consciousness. If we say to ourselves, 'There must be something in man, since this can be revealed to us, and has been revealed to people and people have experienced it; there must be something which makes it possible for man to communicate', then we can ask ourselves another kind of question. If there is another world which is a world of activity, but an incomprehensible activity, something like the picture of a task being accomplished, that is not seen on this earth, is there nothing happening only because we are not able to be conscious of it? Or is there some commerce, some action between these worlds? Is what is beyond consciousness cut off or are we cut off from it? Or is there something happening between the two worlds that is there, affecting us constantly, and which is significant for us, and which is not happening from asking that question. For example, we begin to have, perhaps, a more cautious attitude towards our consciousness, to what happens in ordinary states of consciousness, and to regard them as being concerned with more limited affairs. The other is that we can ask ourselves, 'Is there some other way by which this can be associated with us, with an experience of ours?'

It is probable that everyone here has had some kind of experience that could not be interpreted in terms of their ordinary understanding. They may have remembered it and treasured it, or they may have put it aside and forgotten it, or they may have done something which is not helpful, that is, they have begun to embroider and build upon it and treat it as something which was their own, instead of something which just happened to them at some auspicious moment, when it was possible for it to happen. But if we, all of us, have had some kind of indications that there is something other than this animal life of ours perhaps we can learn about it by doing. It may be that all we have to do is to put aside the expectation that we shall learn about this from our ordinary conscious state, by thinking, by studying, by talking and so on. Perhaps it is through right action that one can learn about this. Perhaps it can be learnt about by the secret of surrendering one's own self-will, by surrendering one's own illusion of being. Perhaps there is the possibility for us of finding things have been understood by people in past times and have been proved to be a means whereby man can open the channels for himself, so that there can be a communication. Perhaps what I am saying is right; that what is beyond consciousness, (and it does mean *beyond* consciousness and not just more consciousness), cannot be expressed in the terms of consciousness. Otherwise the word 'beyond' would cease to have a meaning. At the same time we may also believe that we belong to this, that this is not alien to us, this is not the privilege of a few special saints who happen to have been called or transformed, but that this is in the very nature of man, that he is such a being that this belongs to his nature. This means that he should be a bridge, a connection between the two worlds. If this is so, we should begin to set ourselves to have some confidence in this, and I think that is the real reason why I speak to you about it. It is necessary to go from the idea that there is another world, or a world beyond consciousness, to the idea that there is in man the possibility of the transformation which will carry him through this gap; that there is an action from that other world upon this world. Perhaps we can have all this as ideas. We can even have some conviction and think that it must be like that. From that we can have an operation, a living faith, because faith is by its nature operational. It is the basis of doing. Can we pass to that, living our lives with the thought that there is another world to which we belong, and the thought that our destiny is somehow to be a bridge between the two worlds. To the realisation that it is true that we have a mission in this world; to be a means of transmitting from the other world, finding our own way to it, with two-way traffic. If all these ideas are something to live by as ideas, then can they become something more than that? Can they become operational in us? Can we, at all times and in all that we are doing, have this as the stable centre of our attitudes and choices and decisions? This is what matters, and with this comes a corresponding weakening of our dependence upon external things. Even more important, there comes a weakening of our illusions about ourselves, of our illusions of our own ability to do things, and a readiness to accept that we require the help from this other world. Can we come, by means of contemplating this, to have a strengthening of this part of our nature which bridges these two worlds, and live with that confidence? If we can, then it is of value to us. If it remains as an idea, then it is also very beneficial to us because it is a good antidote against despair.

We do really belong to this whole which is separated by the gulf between the conscious and the beyond conscious, or, as I would also put it, the conditioned, limited world of sense experience, and the unconditioned, unlimited world of that which cannot be reached through the senses. Everything depends on how far we are convinced of this; how far it begins to be part of us.

The difficulty with using imagery is that the imagery is necessarily limiting. If you talk about all possibilities, you are already excluding all impossibilities. All impossibilities *are* nothing. Who knows that this other world is not an impossible world?

I could say something about 'beyond consciousness'. One speaks in terms of a quantitative imagery of everything that exists, 'the all,' and 'all'. You would be quite right in saying that 'all' has no connection with Absolute. If we say that there is something not quantitative at all, not countable at all – when you cannot even say two is different from one – then we have said something that is not easy for the mind to grasp. If we say there is nothing measurable, therefore there is no large and small, we begin to go into a kind of mystical language. I would like to be able to convey to you this sense that I have, that this language is what makes it mystical, not the reality itself.

One can say that mysticism is talking about the ineffable. It is putting into words what cannot be spoken, and therefore it sounds mysteriously extraordinary. The actual experience is something different. That is really why I quoted the story of Bahaeddin's at the beginning, that when the veil was lifted, he did not see some mysterious unknown; he simply saw the teacher of his teacher's teacher sitting there, and he saw that the essential thing was the man who had accomplished the perfecting of his own nature, and that he was inaccessible because people cannot know what it means. They cannot know what is meant by this saying, 'die before you die'. It is one of the *hadiths* of the Prophet; one of the most pithy and condensed sayings that there are. Everything really is contained in this. That which comes from dying, cannot be seen without dying. People say, 'I want to see, but I want to live', but you cannot see what is only seen by dying if you insist on living. You can talk about it. Somebody was talking the other day about the extraordinary experience that she had each time she went to the dentist and was given gas, or whatever it is you have nowadays at dentists'. Each time she saw the whole of reality, and saw the meaning of the whole universe revealed to her. Does one really have to have a toothache in order to

have everything revealed to you? Of course, people can even have
this without a toothache, I do know. I say to you; you go into the
dentist's room and he turns his handle, and your chair goes up and
up and up, and you see over the wall, that there is something on the
other side of the wall. You see there is a marvellous, beautiful garden. And you say, 'I've seen perfection – I've seen what it's like'. You
never say, 'I'm seeing it this moment,' because you don't talk at that
moment, but afterwards. You go to the dentist again and again,
you're wheeled up, you see. But you still remain on this side of the
wall. Then you say, 'This is not good enough – I'm not satisfied with
seeing over this wall,' and you begin going round and the wall is
terribly awkward because it has got many things, weeds and
brambles and bushes and so on all round it, and you see a door. Perhaps you see a door that is quite well cleared, and thousands of
people trying to get in through this door, and you say, 'Well that's
no good', and you go on. And then you see another door that nobody
is bothering about and you perhaps go through that door quite easily
because there is no competition there. You go in through the door
and you are in the garden. This is again a story told by a Sufi. It was
one of the early ones, somebody who lived in Baghdad. 'Yes,' he
said, 'I found this door. It was the door of self-abasement, and
strangely enough nobody was actually crowding round it.'

*What happens if one thinks that there is no door; if one has that
view of life?*

I am not sitting in God's chair; I can't tell whether this is true or
not, but it is said that everyone, at one moment in their lives, sees
the door. To know this for certain, one would have to be God.

*What do you think Rumi meant when he said, 'I have seen that
the two worlds are one?'*

He meant what he said. It is true. Of course it is right. Meister
Eckhart said the same, and so did Jacob Boehme – 'I have seen the
very beginning of the issue of the Trinity from the fountain of God-
head.' But these worlds are only separated because we are confined
to this consciousness. They are not separated in reality. The separation is entirely an illusion of ours. This is what Jalaluddin meant. Of
course they are one world, but in us they are divided, because in us
they have to be re-united. It is the illusion of self, the illusion that
we exist, the illusion that we can know. The difficulty of this illusion
is that we can of course know, and we can know an enormous

amount, and also, in the sense of this kind of existence, we do exist. Therefore this illusion is fastened very firmly on to us. That is why it is said, 'Die before you die'. This is what is meant. Abandon existence before existence abandons you.

*Where should you keep the knowledge of that beyond the veil, or the thought of that beyond the veil, if you are this side of the veil? Should you keep it in your consciousness, or is that a destructive thing? Or should you keep it as a question mark, or where?*

It depends upon what way you are following. There is the way of questioning. There is a way that consists entirely of asking questions, and not giving up. For what did the Buddha sit under the Bhodi tree? He said 'I am not going to get up from this place until this question is answered'. That is not everyone's way. But it does not mean that it is not everyone's business to ask this question and to return to it. You cannot keep it in front of you. We have to assimilate it, so that it has become part of our nature, so that it is truly within us, in our very breathing. That is how this question has to be answered. There has to be the real conviction in us, that this state of existence is not enough. And that does not mean that I want more. When I said 'not enough', I realise that I made a faulty use of language. Obviously I did not mean by that that we must have more existence than we have got now. I simply meant that we have to have this way of living. It is part of man's nature. He is not a being who is special, who has not got any place in this world. Far from it. The quotation from Rumi is quite right. The two worlds are one. The only trouble is that we live too much away from the other world, not that we live too much in this world. We have to live wholly, with full force, in this world. Everything, all that a man can do, we have to do. All that a woman can do, we have to do. No throwing away of this world. But we have to have as much in the other.

At this time there is, in addition to the natural veil, also an unnatural veil. One can say that man is not, for the most part, at the starting point, because we have invented some man-made veils, nylon veils, and these are exceedingly troublesome. Therefore when you say, 'Is this a particular freak of history?', this is the freakish thing; that at this time we human beings, for the most part, have elaborately constructed for ourselves a whole lot of unnecessary veils, so that we not only have the difficulty that is inherent in our nature, of reconciling the conditioned and the unconditioned; we also have a difficulty of reconciling the natural and the unnatural. We have come to something false as well, you understand. We know that this is so; this is historical. It is said that about 4,500 years ago, people were not living in this state of false separation. There was a period when people lived a much more normal life, and therefore there was something different. I am inclined to think that there is something in this.

One must not entirely disregard the notion that we are living in an age of rather greater illusion than the average for man. At a certain period, mankind lives in a state which is nearer to a natural and proper existence and at other times below it. This is the notion of *yugas*, which the Hindus speak about, or the degree of bonding that there is in man. If it is believed, as I believe it, we are now just going through the last throes of this. You have a good chance of living into the beginning of an age of greater light, and I hope to God that all of you will hold on to this and not allow yourself to be drawn back into belief in things as they appear to be. This is the fate of young people; to have a glimpse of the world and how things really are, and then they allow themselves to be concerned with being the managing director of something; or something of that kind.

# Hu

I'm speaking to you with words and you're listening to the words that I'm saying. What I want to convey to you, and what you want to hear from me, cannot be said in words.

So we start with an impossibility. I want to speak about what can't be said, and this I want you to take seriously; when I say that it can't be said, I do mean just that. It can be talked about, but when one talks about it one is talking about an image, an idea or perhaps even nothing more than a lot of words. How far is it beyond words? If it were just one step beyond words, it may be that some sort of analogy, description or picture would help. I'm going to speak about Hu in the sense that the Sufis use this word; in the ordinary way in Arabic it means nothing, 'he', 'she', 'it', anything you like, it just tacks on to the end of verbs and means 'he'. It can be used in the most ordinary way in everyday Arabic conversation. But, it also means the ultimate, that which is entirely beyond all attribute, beyond anything that can ever be said. It also does mean the nearest of all. You've got Nejmeddin Kubra. His explanation of it I can start with. He said 'Every time we breathe, we say this. This "ah" of Allah is the essential reality of everything because everything that breathes, every breath, says this'. This is a way of expressing this immanence, the indwelling of this in everything. One cannot breathe without saying it. That's how he explained it. That's one way of feeling it and experiencing it. It is the very essence of our breathing, that means the very essence of our lives, the very essence of our being. But, for the Sufi, I think it is not so easy to take it in that way alone.

We, for some reason or other, have been put into this world, we've been put into this human body. For me there is no doubt that this has been done for a purpose and we are expected to fulfil that purpose. We've not been sent here for nothing. We haven't even been sent here for our own benefit, but because there is something that is required of us. And, we've been sent about as far away as it is possible to be sent without losing contact with the source, that is without losing the possibility of returning by one's own volition to the Source. If we had been sent further away than this, if we'd been sent into an animal form, or a vegetable form, we wouldn't be able to return of our own accord. We would have had to depend upon the whole evolutionary process to bring us back. Where we are situated, it is just possible to return, that is, to return of our own volition, not by the stream. Everything will return by the stream, but we men are given the possibility of direct return. This state in which we are is in Sufi terms, the *Nasut*. This condition here of existence, which is sometimes called the human condition, really is the human condition together with everything that surrounds us, all this life of the animal, vegetable, mineral world. This is the world to which we've been sent. If we're not able to make our way back by our own volition, it doesn't mean that everything is lost, because we shall return in any case with the stream that flows back to the source. But that's not really what is intended for man. Man's destiny is not just to be carried along in the stream of evolution, through mineral to vegetable, through vegetable to animal, through animal to this kind of life and from this to others. The Source is what we are speaking about : the word Hu.

It is a very restricted world, a very restricted, conditioned state of existence, where we can only see sideways in this world. We see this earth, we see this sun and solar system. We see stars and galaxies. They're all alongside of us. There's no way back through them. The whole of this universe is ordinary. The whole of this universe is subject to the same conditions, the same limitations as our existence. The whole of this visible creation is nothing but this *Nasut*. We think because it is very great, very large in size, because it has existed for thousands of millions of years, that it is something great. It is nothing but one sheet of paper in a great book. But we are hypnotised by this world round us. We can't help somehow or other falling into this illusion that it is because it is large it is great. It's no greater than a sheet of paper put on the floor. Until we can free ourselves from this illusion that this world is great, we find it very difficult to begin to make the journey towards what are the truly great worlds. The truly great worlds are within. It sometimes happens to us that a glimpse comes of this very next world to ours. When that glimpse comes to someone, they are overwhelmed by it. 'This is infinity', they say, 'this is all. Now this is the cosmos revealed'. They call this 'cosmic consciousness'; wonderful, the whole, everything is transformed. Everything is full of wonder and astonishing. Infinity has revealed itself. What has really happened? One little glimpse into a world that is beyond this one! Not even drawn into that world, not even yet coming under the power of that world, and that's what is called 'cosmic consciousness'. You see descriptions of 'cosmic consciousness', they sound wonderful! Visions of infinity, unlimited worlds, beauty beyond telling! 'tis nothing. It is still only just a change of our subjective state. People are drowned again and again in this vision of 'cosmic consciousness'. But what kind of drowning? They just come up and breathe, and everything is just as it was before. All kinds of ecstatic visions, all sorts of wonders, trances and the rest of it, are just nothing else but having added one dimension to our experience. Instead of this flat world in which we live, we have seen some depth, and everything is so changed and transformed by having that perspective in it, that we think this is the reality. 'I have now seen all that there is to see, all has been revealed to me,' – and over and over again people fall into this trap. It is a trap because if they believe in that vision, they will be satisfied with it. If they believe that this is what life is about, to have experiences of cosmic consciousness, of opening of vistas of unspeakable beauty and wonder and so on, then they are caught in that, and just as much caught as we are, as people are, in this material, flat world.

It needs something more. One has to discard, throw away something of oneself, in order to be able really to enter into that world. Then one comes under a different power. Then an action begins. This is called *Jebberut*. The power of God begins to be felt. This is the time when the way is hard. If anyone enters into this, they experience the whole agony of separation, because only then, only when they have gone through this threshold, do they begin to see that they are deprived of everything that really matters, while they are in this state of existence, everything perishable, everything uncertain, conditioned and limited. And really made worse, made more unbearable, when one understands that this vision has given one nothing. The first requirement for this is that one should be able to see that this vision, this 'cosmic consciousness', has done nothing for one. I remember when this happened to me nearly forty years ago now; no it is not so much, not so much, but I remember I thought everything had happened that could happen. For days I was in a state of bliss and ecstasy, and then it, little by little, dawned on me that I was just the same as I had been before. Only then did I really begin to suffer. This is very strange, this second world. A name that is also given to this is the *'Alemi Erwah*. It is called the spiritual world, world of spirits, *Ruh*, the spirit. It is called purgatory, also a name for it. What does it mean? It means the state in which one is aware that one is not able to be what one needs to be, that one is not able to possess what one has seen. Unless you pass through this state, it is impossible; there is no way, I think. Everyone has always said this and the whole of my experience confirms it, that there is no way through, except through this door. Then 'cosmic consciousness' becomes cheap. It is nothing.

What is the worth of it if I am still not able to go the way I must go? I must return to my source, to my origin. Not so many people pass through this door. You must understand that. We talk about it. Everyone who studies Sufism knows all these things that I talk about. What is this, this spiritual world? To enter this, one must be detached, one has to be able to abandon one's attachment to one's body, to one's bodily experiences, to every kind of external support. One has to be as if one had died. Then one can come under that power. This is why it is called *Jebberut*. To be under the power of God. To allow the action of the Divine Power to work on us. People think it is a lovely thing to be purified, to have one's egoism and one's defects cleared out of one. Maybe, but it's not a pleasant thing, not without much suffering. There is no way out. We have to have great respect for those who plunge into this *Istigraq*, the plunge, the going under, letting oneself be taken by this power, letting it act upon one. Then come glimpses of something else. Until that time, the love is truly only a word. It is truly only a word given to something that you don't know, or that you quite wrongly apply to things to which the word love is not a fit word to be given. Only then you see this compassion, this Divine Compassion, which has drawn you into this. This is called the *Melekut*. This is a very high thing. When I first heard about these things and all these words, I can remember how I took them, as if it was something one could know about. But as year after year passed, the more the perspective grew deep and long for me, the more I saw the immensity of this step which enables one to enter into this forecourt of God's presence. We talk about these things, but if you could know how few people can come to it. Not that it's not the Will of God that they should, but that we people have entered into such a state of existence, we've become so much the slaves to every kind of experience that beckons to us, that each time we get caught. You may think but how can people want to be caught in this state of being under this power. Ah yes, but the time comes when things are very different, when there begins to be in this state of *Jebberut* quite a different kind of experiencing, a certain solidity, a certain assurance, that is very alluring. One thinks now I have acquired something, now I am beginning to be something, and we say this, as you know, we say, 'After *fana, baqa*', and we say, 'This is the experience of *fana*; now I know what *baqa* is', but believe me, there are so many deceptive *baqas*, so many deceptive resurrections. How many times I've said to myself, 'I am being born again; now I am rising from the dead', and what did I see? The same man rose again. He never really died. It is then, when you see how many ways we can deceive ourselves. You know, the first deception as I say, is this believing in visions and ecstatic experiences, the opening of 'cosmic consciousness', the complete transformation of everything. The second is one where one begins to feel that there has been death and resurrection in oneself and that something has really happened. And one doesn't see that this is simply a deeper illusion now. If anyone is able to free themselves from the illusion that they have anything, anything at all of their own, that there is any reality other than that, if you can free yourself from this, then for a moment everything changes and you have that experience that there is a quite different God from the one which you ever dreamt of. Quite different and who can't be spoken of any more. You know that not only can't be spoken of but there's no longer a sense of there being a power working or something like this. No longer can anything that you ever said be said any more. That is the threshold, that is the beginning for those who come to it. In Sufism we then say, this leads to the final annihilation, the *fana-i-dhat*. Everything disappears. Not only oneself, but the world and God all disappear. Then we say this is Hu. We say: this is *huwiyet*. This is that state. (*Huwiyet* is the word for a state.) The state when that which came from the source has re-entered the source. *Huwiyet*, that is how I pronounce it. If I were an Arab, I would pronounce it differently. That state is for Sufis the way of speaking of the end, the final liberation from everything that separates.

Now, how are these things possible? We've got instruments; eyes and ears and the rest, to know about this external world. We've got minds to think abou this world. We've got minds to think and make pictures and form concepts of other worlds, and we don't see that these minds have their source, not in anything above or higher. They have no future, no destiny. They are simply the instruments of this world. It is hard for us to accept the idea that the mind must be annihilated, that everything we have that thinks, that feels, that knows, that sees and hears, all these are the instruments of imprison-ment within this world. It happens, tomorrow morning early I am off to India, to take part in the celebration of the hundredth anniver-sary of Sri Aurobindo's birth. I mention Aurobindo because Auro-bindo was a great prophet of this time and his great message was the message of what he called the Supramental, and he spoke of the 'descent of the supramental at this time'. A clumsy kind of word, but it is an important thing, because he at least got over to a large num-ber of people that our human mind is a totally inadequate instru-ment for arriving at any real understanding. That it is only when it is possible to plunge beyond the mind that anything happens, and it is this moment of plunging beyond the mind that reveals to us this, what we call, 'cosmic consciousness'. But how do we have this 'cos-mic consciousness', if it's not possible for our minds to have it? Be-cause we have other instruments. Because we are not created just with a mind. This is a cheap instrument, this human mind. Cheap in terms of the path to reality. It is not cheap for this world. It gives us immense power in this world, it enables us to dominate in this world; but it is cheap when you look at the other world. But we people were not intended just for this. So we've been given instruments. We've been given an instrument, a spiritual instrument which is able to live and enter into this second world, this, what we call *Jebberut*, the *'Alemi Erwah*, the world of spirits. We have a spiritual percep-tion. We have to awaken these spiritual perceptions.

They will awaken in us partly through the intense need that one begins to feel when this first shows itself to us, the intense need to be able to experience this other reality, and not only to experience it. This is in the long run, or not very long run either, utterly dis-satisfying. One cannot accept merely to see and not to possess what one loves. So that is the first thing. This is where your patron Ibn 'Arabi was a great teacher. He taught the necessity for man to awaken and strengthen and learn to use and live with these finer instruments. He achieved it himself and he brought many, many people to the conviction that this is indeed possible for us. You mustn't think that you can enter purgatory with this body and mind. If you want to enter that world, this *Jebberut*, you have to enter it with your spiritual nature, not with your natural self. But this spiritual nature of ours is in dire trouble. Don't think that just because we have a spiritual nature, that this spiritual nature has only to be awakened and released and it is already able to find its goal. No. Our spiritual nature is tainted, tainted with our own egoism, tainted with our own illusions, tainted with our craving for existence, our holding on to externals. All this is in the spiritual nature, not only in our physical nature. There has to be awakened in us the instrument, the spiritual instrument that can see how it is with us, and that is a very great suffering. But, it is also, as this spiritual instrument of ours begins to awaken and we begin to see that the realities are so extraordinary that everything else ceases to matter. Only one thing, to possess that.

Then comes the time when yet another instrument, a higher instrument still, an instrument which is not spiritual but Divine, an instrument that is lent to us, or given to us, or somehow we're drawn to it. I don't know how to speak of that. But this Divine instrument then allows us to go beyond all this and to see that the whole of this existence is nothing. This is nothing but a shadow, a play. Then comes quite a different kind of thing, quite a different kind of opening. This has to be. I've simplified the talk because many people as you know speak of it in different stages and so on. There are many ways and what I say is just one way of speaking about it. If I spoke about it tomorrow, I would speak about it differently, because this can never be said the same way twice.

Why do I say all this to you? Because I wanted, when I asked if I could come and speak to you, I wanted to say one thing only to you, but I had to prepare all this, and that is that I want to ask you to have an unlimited respect always present in you for the word Hu. Sometimes I suffer when I hear the word Hu, the syllable Hu, used lightly. I must tell you, because I am no friend of yours if I don't speak to you truly.

I came with many of you who are here, I think, to that festival that was near Glastonbury. And I saw people dancing round and joining hands with people as if it was a sort of country dance and

chanting *Ya Hu*, or *Allah Hu*. You know the words *Allah Hu* cannot
be spoken like that. It is not right. If the word *Allah Hu* is pro-
nounced, the whole depth of one's being must be stirred by it. You,
all of you, wear symbols, symbolising this breath of life, this breath
which is far more than that, the word Hu. But you've chosen and
you've taken this supreme symbol of the source of everything, the
ultimate that is beyond everything and you are not respecting it as
you should. You think you are. You know that for many many years I
didn't dare to pronounce the word God. There were some words that
I couldn't bring myself to pronounce, the word God, the word Love,
I just couldn't bring to my lips, because I felt so far away from them.
Then little by little, I don't know whether because I have grown
hard and callous, or whether because I have penetrated more deeply,
God knows, but I began to use these words. I try to use them with
deep respect. But of all words, the one perhaps of all sounds, the one
to be most respected is the word Hu. Because it stands for everything. It stands for that which is in every breath we breathe, and it
stands for the source which can only be reached by complete annihilation of everything, because it is beyond all existence, beyond all
being. You will have to use the word, but I came here to beg you to
remember, that you have chosen the holiest syllable that there is and
if you've done that, you've taken on yourself a great responsibility.
If you treat it without this respect, it is sacrilege. It is only the fewest
of the few, the rarest of the rare actually come to the reality of Hu.
The very great chosen ones, chosen and sent; messengers. Only they
can really say the word Hu. Those who come directly from the
source and will return to the source. They know what Hu is. So you
must forgive me if I speak in that way and I did ask permission
to do this. I was not invited. I thrust myself on you in that way
and I came because this power which must be obeyed, *al Muti*, who
must be obeyed, made me come. There is within us all this power.
But to be able to listen to and be obedient to that power, we must
put aside all visible and thinkable things.

# Glossary

*Abdal:* The Forty : they act in direct service to the Qutb of the time as 'substitutes' for Saints. They control in various ways the destiny of the world. p. 61.

*Abdul Qadir Gilani:* the spiritual founder and 'Pir' of the Qadiri order of dervishes and one of the greatest and most powerful mystics of all time (he was called the Gauth el A'zam'). His tomb is in Baghdad. p. 49.

*Abu Bakr:* the prophet's closest friend. He was the first Caliph, from A.D. 632 until A.D. 634. p. 71.

*Allah:* God : the sum of the Divine Names, pp. 37, 90, 97.

*'alemi edjsam:* the world (universe) of bodies. pp. 31, 72.

*'alemi erwah:* the world (universe) of spirits. pp. 19, 39, 72, 93.

*'alemi imkan:* the world (universe) of possibilities. pp. 30, 38, 74.

*'alemi jebberut:* the world (universe) of compulsion. p. 19.

*'alemi nebati:* the world (universe) of vegetation. p. 19.

*Ali:* the 4th Caliph who reigned for 4 years and 9 months during a period of great unrest. He was the Prophet's cousin and son-in-law, and is known to certain Sufis as 'The Gateway to Knowledge'. p. 71.

*Ana'l Hacq:* 'I am the Truth' – Hallaj. p. 82.

*Arupa Loka:* the formless world. p. 72.

*Aurobindo:* See : 'Shri Aurobindo, The Story of His Life' published by the Shri Aurobindo Ashram, Pondicherry, India. p. 95.

*a'yan al thabita:* immutable possibilities. p. 31. See : 'The Wisdom of the Prophets' by Ibn 'Arabi – Beshara Publications.

*Bahaeddin Naqsheband:* the spiritual founder and 'Pir' of the Naqshebandi order of dervishes, a rather strict but very large order or 'Tariqa' which has many branches and offshoots. pp. 52, 78.

*baraqah:* benediction, spiritual influence. p. 58.

*baqa:* enduring, everlasting. pp. 28, 37, 94.

*Bismillah er Rahman er Rahim:* in the Name of God, The Merciful, The Compassionate. p. 39.

*Boehme, Jakob:* (1575-1624) a German mystic who asserted both the transcendence and immanence of God. His works were denounced by the church as heretical. p. 87.

*Bruno, Giordano:* an Italian mystic burned at the stake during the Inquisition. p. intro.

*chakra:* a centre of the psychic body. p. 51.

*Conference of the Birds:* an allegorical mystical book written by Farid ud-din Attar, p. 28.

*dervish:* a poor man, humble, modest in spirit. Also a member of one of the esoteric orders operating within the Islamic tradition. p. 41.

*Dionysius:* the Areopagite. Work written in his name around A.D. 500 became very important to the theology and spirituality of Eastern Orthodoxy and Western Catholicism. p. 72.

*Eckhart, Meister* (Johannes 1260?-1327): a German philosopher and mystic. p. 87.

*fana:* annihilation, impermanence. pp. 28, 37, 94.

*fana-i-af'al:* annihilation of effects. p. 37.

*fana-i-ahkam:* annihilation of attributes, predications. p. 38.

*fana-i-dhat:* annihilation of essences. pp. 37, 94.

*fana-i-sifat:* annihilation of qualities. p. 37.

*genii/jinn:* beings of non-human substance existing on the same plane as human life and possessing both good and evil characteristics. p. 73.

*Gilani:* (see Abdul Qadir Gilani).

*Gita:* Bhagavad Gita : the Hindu sacred book of the 4th Century B.C. p. 37.

*Gücdüvânî, Abdülhalik:* one of the greatest Sheikhs of the Haja Gân. The Qutb of his time, he was so powerful that it has been said that if he had been alive at the time of Al-Hallaj, Hallaj need not have said 'Ana'l Hacq' (I am the Truth). p. 79.

*haqq (haqiqah):* the Truth. p. 78.

*hadith:* sayings, traditions (of the Prophet). pp. 21, 25, 28, 30.

*Haja Gân:* a 'dynasty' of Sufi 'arafin' (masters) dating from the 9th Century centred in the Bokhara region and known as the 'Masters of Wisdom'. p. intro.

*halka:* the 'Circle of Friends' as in Sufi ceremonies. p. 51.

*Hallaj:* the great mystic who was crucified in A.D. 921 for saying 'Ana'l Hacq' (I am the Truth). p. 49.

*Hu:* the First Sound or annunciation of the Ipseity. pp. 37, 74, 97.

*Husam al-Din:* the first leader of the followers of Jelaluddin Rumi after his death. p. 78.

*huwiyet:* Essence. pp. 37, 94.

*Iblis:* the Devil. p. 73.

*Ibn 'Arabi, Sheikh Muhyi-d-Din:* the 12th Century mystic known as 'The Pole (Qutb) of Knowledge', and 'The Greatest Sheikh'. pp. 31, 66.

*insan:* Man. pp. 19, 58.

*ism-i-azam:* The Greatest Name. p. 36.

*istigraq:* drowning, union. p. 93.

*jebberut:* compulsion. pp. 66, 74, 92.

*khalifah:* Successor, Viceregent. p. 78.

*khayal:* pertaining to the realm of imagination, ideas, concepts, apparitions, shadows. p. 22.

*Khidr:* the 'eternal guide' associated with Elijah and sometimes referred to in other traditions as 'The Green Man'. pp. 40, 68.

*Magi:* men of Wisdom, sages. Members of the ancient Persian priestly caste. pp. 21, 75.

*mantram:* word or words used by Hindus and Buddhists in prayer chants. p. 40.

*Mathnawi:* of Jelaluddin Rumi. His book of mystical poetry consisting of 30,000 couplets (translation and commentary by R. A. Nicholson). p. 83.

*melekut:* Angelic forms. pp. 66, 69, 93.

*Mevlevis:* known as the 'whirling' or 'dancing' dervishes. The followers of Mevlâna – Jelaluddin Rumi. pp. 52, 78.

*Mount Hira:* a mountain near Mecca to which the Prophet Muhammed went for meditation and spiritual retreat in his early life. p. 48.

*Muhammed el-Amin:* the Prophet Muhammed, 'el-Amin' The Trusted One. pp. 48, 79.

*Mutassarif al zaman:* dispenser of Divine Will of the time. Under him are categories of men directed to carry out the Divine Will. p. 61.

*Muti-al-Muti:* The Obedient One. p. 97.

*mutma 'in:* tranquil, at rest, peace of mind. p. 22.

*nafs al ammârah:* commanding soul. pp. 58, 62.

*Nejmeddin Kubra:* the spiritual founder and 'Pir' of the Kubrawi order of dervishes in Iran in the 7th Century. p. 90.

*namaz:* ('sabat' in Arabic), prayers, devotions, worship. p. 25.

*Naqshebandis:* an order of dervishes. The followers of Muhammed Bahaeddin Naqsheband. pp. 52, 78.

*nasut:* human aspect, form. pp. 66, 69, 91.

*Nineveh:* the ancient capital of the Assyrian Empire. p. 60.

*nirvana:* a Buddhist term meaning literally 'blowing out' or extinction. It is also found in Vedanta to express union with Brahma. p. 74.

*Pali Pitakas:* 'Pali' is the sacred language of the Southern Buddhists. 'Pitakas' (literally, baskets) of which there are three containing the doctrines of early Buddhism. p. 73.

*Qutb al zaman:* the 'Pole' of the time. p. 61.

*Qutb:* the one who acts as complete Viceregent of God, and whose identity is never revealed. p. 61.

*ruh:* Spirit. pp. 19, 63, 93.

*ruhani:* pertaining to the Spirit. p. 63.

*Rumi, Jelaluddin:* the poet and mystic and 'Pir' of the Mevlevi order of dervishes, and known as 'The Pole (Qutb) of Love'. pp. 78, 83, 87.

*Rupa Loka:* the world of forms. p. 72.

*salik:* The Seeker. p. 33.

*Shamzi Tabriz:* the 'Sun of Tabriz', a mysterious dervish from Persia who inspired and taught Jelaluddin Rumi in Konya. p. 61.

*shari'ah:* the formal religious dogma of Islam. p. 71.

*Sheikh (Shaykh):* a man of spiritual authority and a teacher. p. 51.

*Shiva Puri Baba:* an Indian sage described in 'The Long Pilgrimage' by J. G. Bennett. Shiva Puri Baba lived to be over 130 years old. p. 41.

*sobat:* companionship, benefiting from company. p. 66.

*Sura (sûrat):* chapter, picture, or a particular section (as in the Koran). p. 24.

*Sushupti:* in Hindu philosophy the stage before complete union. pp. 39, 80.

*tahbib:* (derived from the Arabic 'hub' meaning love), the power of attraction allowing, encouraging love (of God). p. 21.

*Tao:* literally the 'way'. Taoism – the Oriental philosophy and religion as taught by Lao Tseu. p. 35.

*taslim:* surrender. p. 38.

*tawakkul:* putting trust in God. p. 41.

*Terevadin Buddhists of the Nikayas:* the Southern Buddhists who follow the Pali Pitakas. p. 81.

*Wakil:* Protector, Agent. p. 39.

*Wali:* Saint. p. 65.

*wiswas:* diabolical suggestion, temptation by the devil. p. 24.

*Ya:* term of exclamation. p. 97.

*Yezidis:* the followers of Yezid, the instigator of the murder of the Prophet's two grandsons. p. 60.

*Yoga:* literally 'union' or 'yoke'. A system of practices in Hindu philosophy and religion. p. 37.

*Yogi:* one who practises Yoga. p. 41.

*Yugas:* the 4 ages or eras of evolution. p. 89.

*Zikr:* a devotional remembrance of God by repetition of the Divine Names. A ritual practice essential and common to all dervish orders. p. 36.

*Zoroastrians:* the followers of the religion of Zoroaster. p. 75.